SAFETY MANAGEMENT FOR LANDSCAPERS, GROUNDS-CARE BUSINESSES AND GOLF COURSES

Perfect training tool using the safest way to operate outdoor power equipment. Loaded with illustrations and true-to-life stories.

FUNDAMENTALS OF SERVICE

PUBLISHER

DEERE & COMPANY, JOHN DEERE PUBLISHING
One John Deere Place
Moline, IL 61265
http://www.deere.com/deerecom/Farmers+and+Ranchers/Publications
1-800-522-7448

JOHN DEERE PUBLISHING STAFF
Cindy S. Calloway
Sharon Clapp

TO THE READER: The goal of this book is to prevent injuries and save lives. But it will accomplish this only if you read carefully and heed the safety advice. Understand some important safety information is not in this book - it's in your equipment's operator's manual. Be sure you've read the operator's manual for each machine you run.

If you don't know a word check the Glossary. Glossary words are in **bold faced** in the copy. We hope you read and enjoy *Safety Management for Landscapers, Grounds-Care Businesses and Golf Courses*. It will help make you and your fellow workers smarter and safer.

ACKNOWLEDGEMENTS:

Author: Rodney J. Gasch, Writer, Evans City PA

Consulting Editors: David E. Baker, Safety Specialist, University of Missouri, Columbia, MO, Dick Depauw, Product Safety Engineer, Deere & Company, Moline, IL, Dr. Carol J. Lehtola, Extension Agricultural Safety Specialist, University of Florida, Gainesville, FL, Gary Mills, Product Safety Training, Deere & Company, Moline, IL

Copy Editor: Randy Stephens

Special Acknowledgements: The author wishes to express his gratitude to the following individuals who provided vital advice and support. Donna Chermak, Editor, St. Paul MN 55116, William and Noah Gasch, Evans City Pa, Laurie Kirsch, Evans City Pa, Dr. Charles Schwab, Extension Safety Specialist, Iowa State University, Ames IA, Debbie Schwiebert, e-Business, Deere & Company, Moline, IL, Janis Stone, Ph.D., Textiles and Clothing, Iowa State University, Ames IA

Contributors: Special thanks to the following persons and organizations who provided literature, digital images, and technical assistance. Erica Castle, University of Missouri, Columbia, MO; Robert Coats, American Honda Motor Co., Alpharetta, GA; Allen Edwards, John Deere Worksite Products, Knoxville TN; Jim Fear, The Toro Company, Bloomington MN; Jim Fennel, American Honda Motor Co. , Alpharetta GA; Mark Ford, John Deere Company, Raleigh, NC; Mark Holland, MTD Products, Cleveland OH; Steve Johnson, John Deere Commercial Porducts, Augusta GA; Patty King, Outdoor Power Equipment Institute, Old Town Alexandria VA; Dave Knight, John Deere Commercial Products, Augusta GA; Robin Korneff, Sysco, Harmony PA; Murry Madsen, Deere & Company, Moline IL; Liz Petrus, Gempler's, Bellville, WI; Mike Scaletta, John Deere Company, Raleigh NC; Terry Skelton, John Deere Commercial Products, Augusta GA; Mary Weston, The Toro Company, Bloomington MN; Gregg Wittenberger, Viking Trailers, Renfrew PA; Nancy Young, National Farm Medicine Center, Marshfield WI; Clay Yeatman, American Honda Motor Co., Duluth GA.

OTHER MANUALS IN THE SERIES: The FOS series covering compact equipment systems consists of the following manuals:

• Engines
• Electrical Systems
• Hydraulics
• Power trains

FOR MORE INFORMATION: This book is one of many books published on agricultural and industrial machinery. For more information or to request a FREE CATALOG call 1-800-522-7448 or send your request to: Deere Company, John Deere Publishing, One John Deere Place, Moline IL 61265 or:

Visit Us on the Internet—
http://www.deere.com/aboutus/pub/jdpub/

We have a
long-range interest in
Agribusiness Management

ISBN 0-86691-250-9

CONTENTS

4 ORGANIZING A SAFETY PROGRAM

5 COMPACT TRACTORS

6 LOADERS, BACKHOE ATTACHMENTS, AND SKID-STEER LOADERS

7 COMMON ATTACHMENTS FOR COMPACT TRACTORS

8 ROTARY MOWERS AND CUTTERS

9 LAWN-GROOMING EQUIPMENT

13 *SPRAYING EQUIPMENT*

14 *UTILITY VEHICLES*

15 *TRANSPORTING OUTDOOR POWER EQUIPMENT*

16 *SAFETY IN THE MAINTENANCE SHOP*

WHY STUDY SAFETY?

INTRODUCTION

Since you are reading this book, you obviously have some interest in safety. That's great!

But, just in case you are reading this book because a teacher, boss, or safety inspector told you to, here are three good reasons to study safety:

- **to prevent injuries**
- **to prevent financial losses**
- **to prevent fines and penalties.**

PREVENT INJURIES

To prevent injuries, equipment needs to be properly maintained with all safety devices in working order, plus every operator needs to know the safe way to run the equipment. All too often that's not the case.

Consider these depressing statistics:

In an average week in the United States:

- **1,400 people are injured with lawn mowers.**
- **600 people are injured with chain saws.**
- **700 people are injured by pruning, edging, and trimming equipment.**
- **6 people are killed because of tractor mishaps.**

Source: 2000 Injury Facts, National Safety Council

Sadly, the vast majority of these injuries don't have to happen. In most cases, people were hurt because operators weren't properly clothed or outfitted with protective gear, weren't properly trained, or were trained but decided to ignore the training.

Studying this book, and other safety materials, will make you more aware of the general risks of operating grounds-maintenance equipment. That's good, but it's not good enough. At a minimum, every operator should read the operator manual before a machine is ever started. If you haven't read the operator manual, you won't know the proper protective clothing to wear, the proper way to hold or operate the machine, and you won't know the potential hazards present on the machine.

Plus, the operator manual tells you how equipment must be serviced and maintained to operate properly. A machine that is properly tuned and maintained is less likely to be involved in a mishap.

If the operator manual is missing, contact your equipment dealer or the equipment's manufacturer. Replacement operator manuals are usually available for a small charge.

Fig. 1 – Before You Ever Operate a Machine You Should Read the Operator Manual

Besides reading the operator manual, it's important to get familiar with the equipment before you actually do any work.

With hand-held machines, that might mean holding and moving the machine with the engine shut off. For a self-propelled lawn mower, it may mean practicing the controls with the blade not engaged. This will help you develop operating skills before you actually get into a work situation. It's important to feel comfortable with a machine's operation before you actually do any work.

Fig. 2 – This Operator is Practicing Driving a Self-Propelled Lawn Mower with the Blade Disengaged

People buy grounds-care equipment because it can do jobs faster and better than by hand. But to do the job faster and better, the equipment must use powerful engines and motors, and fast turning drives, blades and tines. All these things pose potential hazards.

By studying proper operating procedures and then putting what you've learned into action, you can greatly eliminate the risk of one of those hazards causing an injury. Ignore safe operating procedures, and you're on the road to becoming one of the many injury statistics.

This Could Be You...While injury statistics tell us something about why to study safety, there is a more personal side to why safety is important. Throughout this book we will be retelling stories of people injured in equipment mishaps. We do this to underscore the personal cost of these incidents, not just in terms of lost work, or hospital costs, but in terms of human pain and suffering.

Here's one such story...Kimberly had a party to go to, and just a quarter acre of mowing to do before she could call it quits. Unfortunately, a traffic jam had delayed her getting to this client. Now it was after 7 p.m., and not only was it getting darker by the minute, the grass was getting more and more damp. But she couldn't stop cutting now, not with just a quarter acre more to do. The incident happened fast. The discharge chute on the riding mower had clogged for the fifth time. But this time, instead of getting off the mower, Kimberly kept on mowing and just reached down to shake the chute. As she stretched, her wet boot slipped off the footrest and suddenly she lost her balance. Her hand was headed right for the mower blades. When her weight left the seat, the engine shut off immediately. That probably saved her hand. As it was, the tips of three fingers were cut off. Instead of going to a party, she spent most of the evening in the emergency room.

PREVENT FINANCIAL LOSSES

Another reason to study safety is to prevent financial losses.

Mishaps are very expensive – certainly in terms of human suffering, but also in terms of money spent. A trip to the emergency room, or a day in the hospital can run from hundreds to thousands of dollars, depending upon the injury and the care needed.

One operator, ignoring one safety rule, or taking one short cut, can generate huge hospital bills.

These mishaps are also expensive for employers. Unfortunately many employers don't realize just how expensive.

Employer costs can be divided into two categories – **direct costs** and **indirect costs**. Direct costs cover just two important areas – medical expenses for the injured employee, and the employee's lost wages. Often direct costs are covered by **worker's compensation**, or some other insurance. Since these expenses are the most visible and easiest to add up, they are sometimes the only cost an employer considers.

This is an important business mistake. In reality, indirect costs almost always end up far greater than direct costs.

Indirect or hidden costs include such things as:

- **downtime of fellow workers after a mishap.**
- **overtime to make up for a lost employee.**
- **reduced employee efficiency and morale.**
- **time spent filling out reports.**
- **time spent filling out insurance forms.**
- **efforts to hire and train a replacement worker.**
- **possible fines if the incident resulted in a safety inspection.**

These indirect costs can total 4 to 10 times as much as the direct costs of an injury.

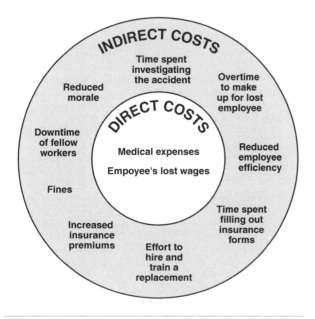

Fig. 3 – The Total Financial Loss from a Mishap Includes Direct and Indirect Costs

As you can see, injuries can be very expensive for business. By contrast, properly maintaining equipment and properly training operators is relatively cheap.

It makes financial sense for business to have an active safety program (see Chapter 4). And certainly it makes sense for workers to be involved in such programs. Often, because of the involvement, worker performance will improve. But more importantly, these programs can save not only money, they can also save a toe, a hand or perhaps a life.

This Could Be You...After three years in the lawn care business things are going well for Javier. At least they were until Judd got injured. Judd was part of a 3-person crew that mowed lawns at several office parks and strip malls. The summer had been pretty uneventful until that Monday morning when Judd's string trimmer picked up a small stone. The stone ricocheted off a building and into Judd's eye. Judd was not wearing safety glasses, even though company policy required them. The company's insurance covered the medical bill, but other business costs continue to hurt Javier's profits. Since Judd's co-workers took him to the emergency room, they both missed a half-day of mowing. Judd missed two weeks of work, so other crewmembers had to work overtime to cover for him. Judd's co-workers are now overly cautious when using the string trimmer. Even though they both now wear their safety glasses, their trimming time has been doubled. Perhaps even more worrisome, Judd's brother just graduated from law school. What kind of advice is he giving Judd? To think all of this could have been prevented with a pair of safety-glasses.

PREVENT FINES AND PENALTIES

A third reason to study safety – it's the law.

In 1970 the U.S. Congress passed, and President Richard Nixon signed into law, the **OSHA** Act. It established the Occupational Safety and Health Administration whose goal is "to assure, so far as possible, every working man and woman in the nation safe and healthful working conditions."

Fig. 4 – OSHA Regulations Require Employers to Provide a Workplace Free of Serious Hazards

Except for certain specific exclusions, the act applies to every employer who has one or more employees and who are in a business affecting interstate commerce. For all practical matters, all landscapers, grounds-care businesses, and golf courses are covered under the Act.

Under OSHA regulations, employers have the general duty to provide each employee with employment that is free from recognized hazards that cause, or are likely to cause, death or serious physical harm. In other words, employers are expected to provide safe equipment and a safe place to work.

Each employee, in turn, is expected to comply with rules and safety and health standards.

Since OSHA regulations are extensive and do change, we won't cover specific OSHA rules and regulations in much detail. But it is important to realize the law is out there, and that you are probably affected. That's one more reason to study and practice safety. (Some OSHA information is covered in Chapter 4. For additional information concerning regulations, contact your trade association, or your Regional OSHA office. Check the OSHA website, www.osha.gov.)

This Could Be You...The water project was going well. The new supply line for the irrigation system had been laid and it was just a matter of grading a little dirt. Pete hopped on the tractor and used the rear blade to smooth out the uneven line of soil that ran between the road and the ravine. Pete didn't fasten his seat belt. No one ever did at the golf course. In fact, on this tractor Pete couldn't have fastened his seat belt even if he had wanted to. Part of the buckle had been bent several years ago so that the buckle parts no longer mated. Pete hadn't graded 20 feet when the edge of the ravine suddenly gave way. The tractor started to roll, tossing Pete out of the seat, and directly into its path. The right fender caught him in the abdomen, pinning him down as the tractor slid some 50 feet down the embankment. The ambulance was there within 10 minutes, but it was too late. Pete never regained consciousness.

AVOIDING MISHAPS IS NOT COMMON SENSE

Finally, it's important to realize proper safety procedures are generally not something you can just pick up from co-workers, or know automatically by "using your head." Too many experienced workers have developed their own set of bad safety habits. And contrary to what some people think, working safely is not just using your common sense.

Safety is something you need to practice and something you need to learn and review. Each new season can present you with a new machine to operate. Each new machine can present you with a new set of potential hazards (see Chapter 3). And each new situation can present it's own safety challenges.

There are many reasons to study safety – perhaps as many reasons as there are victims. Continue your study and there's a great likelihood you will stay healthy and stay wealthy.

Fig. 5 – Safety Alert Symbol

Machines themselves provide safety messages through the safety alert symbol (above) and signal words.

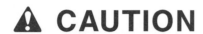

CAUTION
1. Keep all shields in place.
2. Disengage and shut off all engine and/or motor power before servicing or unclogging machine.
3. Keep hands, feet, and clothing away from power-driven parts.

Fig. 6 – Caution Symbol

CAUTION is used to remind operators of safety instructions that must be followed, and to identify less serious hazards. Caution signs are yellow.

WARNING
Keep all shields in place.
Keep hands and clothing away from rotating fan.

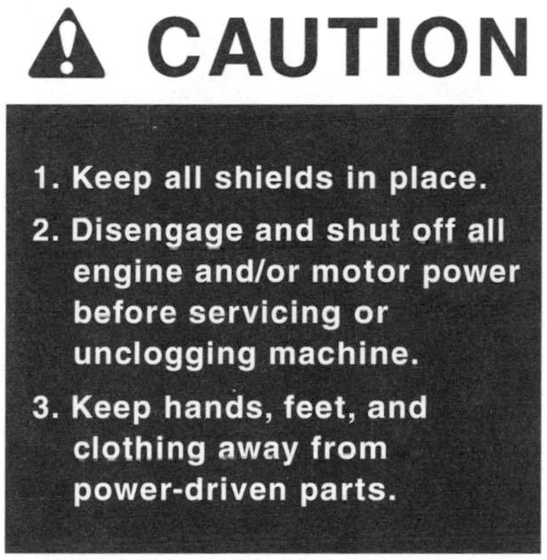

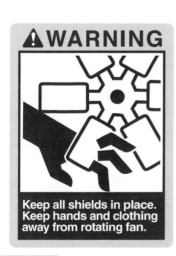

Fig. 7 – Warning Symbol

WARNING means the hazard presents a lesser degree of risk of serious injury or death. Warning signs are usually orange.

DANGER
ROTATING BLOWER
●SHUT OFF ENGINE BEFORE UNCLOGGING DISCHARGE CHUTE

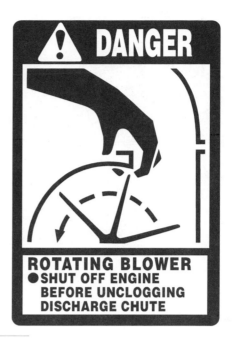

Fig. 8 – Danger

DANGER alerts you to one of the most serious potential hazards. Exposure to a "danger" hazard would result in a high probability of death or severe injury. Danger signs are red.

TEST YOURSELF

QUESTIONS - CHAPTER 1

1. List three reasons to study safety.
2. What is the difference between direct and indirect costs?
3. What agency of the government is charged with overseeing workplace safety?

HUMAN FACTORS

INTRODUCTION

Many factors go into preventing an equipment injury. In this chapter we'll look at the human factors. Human factors include how the human body reacts to work, to the environment, and to outdoor power equipment. We study human factors to understand people's limitations to perform a task.

If we were robots, these reactions would be of little concern. You can program a robot to perform a task and know it will perform that task over and over with no regard for the weather, day of the week, or emotional state.

But you won't see robots taking on many landscaping and golf course jobs. That's because there are so many variables involved in this work that it takes a human brain and body to properly do the job.

Fig. 1 — Robots can Perform Routine Tasks in the Controlled Setting of a Factory

But human brains and bodies have their limitations. All bodies are not created equal. They come in many shapes and sizes. And a person's brain is not always up to the task of making good decisions. Fatigue, moods, and many other variables can affect human decisions.

That's why it's important to understand the human factors that go into making a good operator. We're not talking about proper training here. Instead, we're talking about factors like strength, eyesight, and reaction time. If you better understand how your body works and interacts with equipment, you'll better understand how to be a safe operator.

In this chapter we'll also look at personal protective equipment **(PPE)** and the potential dangers of using equipment near other people.

HUMAN LIMITATIONS

Employers like a worker with a can-do attitude. Someone who is ready and willing to tackle a task. But it's important to realize a can-do attitude that doesn't consider personal limitations can cause injuries. For your safety it's important to know your own personal limitations and understand how they can change during the day.

Factors that influence personal limitations include:

- **strength**
- **reaction time**
- **body size**
- **age**
- **fatigue**
- **drugs**
- **tobacco**
- **alcohol**

STRENGTH

It's no secret that some people are stronger than others. Yet many workers will hesitate to ask for help when a task requires lots of brawn. Trying to tackle a job that's bigger than you are is like picking a fight with someone who's bigger than you are. There's a good chance you'll get hurt. Know your strength limits and get help if you need it.

Also remember your strength is not constant throughout the day. It changes depending on the tasks you have been doing. Muscles become tired quickly doing tasks that require a lot of energy. This means a task you can handle first thing in the morning may be too much for you at the end of the day, or after a period of strenuous work.

DIFFERENCES IN SIZE AND STRENGTH

Fig. 2 – Different People have Different Abilities. Understand your Limitations

That's why it's important to recognize your strength limitations. Don't demand too much of your muscles. A muscle strained to its maximum tires quickly. And tired muscles may not respond readily if they are needed to avoid a mishap.

You should also take frequent, short breaks. A good guideline is 10 minutes of rest or reduced activity for every two hours of heavy work. Short, frequent breaks are more effective in recovering working ability than longer, infrequent breaks.

REACTION TIME

How fast can you react to a sudden problem? Chances are not as fast as you think. Before your body can react to a problem, a series of physical and mental events must occur.

First a sensor (eyes, ears, nose, or skin) sends a message to the brain. Then the brain analyzes that information and decides what action to take, and sends out a message to your muscles to take the appropriate action.

For example, a tractor driver may see an obstacle up ahead. The operator's brain analyzes the message and decides on a course of action—stop the tractor, or drive around the obstacle, or ignore the obstacle. Then the brain must tell the proper muscles to carry out the decision. That all takes time. Anyone who has ever mistakenly picked up something that was extremely hot knows it takes a while for the brain to tell the hand, "let go!

The best human reactions are slow compared to the speed and power of machinery.

Assume a reaction time of three-fourths of a second. In that time:

- **A typical lawn mower blade makes 75 cuts.**
- **A tooth on a chain saw travels 66 feet.**
- **A tractor tipping backwards has reached its point of no return.**

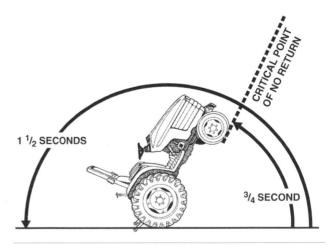

Fig. 3 – A Rear-tipping Tractor can reach its Point of no Return in Three -fourths of a Second or Less. That's Too Fast for You to React and Jump Clear.

How do you improve your reaction time? Your reactions will be quicker if you come to work well rested, take short breaks during the day, and avoid tobacco, alcohol, and drugs.

But it's probably more important to just accept the fact you can't depend on quick reactions to save you from an injury. Never take chances thinking that your amazingly quick reactions will protect you. It just doesn't work that way.

BODY SIZE

Most equipment is designed so it can be adjusted to accommodate a wide variety of body shapes and sizes. But generally these adjustments don't happen automatically. Make sure the equipment you use is properly set for your body size.

For example, most commercial line trimmers use an over-the-shoulder strap for support. If the strap is not adjusted to the right length, the trimmer will be much more difficult and tiring to operate. Read the operator's manual to understand how to get your equipment set right for your body.

Fig. 4 — Make Sure Equipment is Properly Adjusted for your Body Size

AGE

Your physical capabilities reach their optimum when you're 25 to 30 years of age and then they slowly decline. Judgment and skill, based on experience, usually continue to increase well beyond age 30. This can often offset the increases in reaction time and decreases in muscle strength that naturally occur as we age.

However, somewhere between 55 and 70 the typical person's eyesight, hearing, and strength deteriorate to the point that performance is poorer than it was at younger ages. People who reach this stage often fail to recognize or admit their decreased abilities and continue to try to work as they did in their younger years. These people are at greater risk of going beyond their capabilities and having or causing an injury.

What's important is not how old you are, but rather that you recognize your personal limitations and adjust your work behavior accordingly.

FATIGUE

Everyone has felt fatigued at one time or another. You may have worked or exercised to the point that your body could no longer continue. That's because the more you increase your physical output, the more blood flow and respiration must increase to supply muscles with needed energy and oxygen. When muscles work at a rate exceeding the ability of the heart and lungs, aching muscles, cramping, tremor, and finally, loss of control may result. You just have to stop and rest to recover.

Fatigue is like a safety device that keeps muscles from working beyond their capacity. Individual motivation and desire play a very significant role in determining this limit. Strong motivation pushes the limit far beyond the normal one, but there is a limit.

"TAKE A BREAK! I'LL TAKE OVER."

Fig. 5 – Fatigue can Cause Danger to You and Others - Know your Limitations

If you reach this limit and continue to work, you are more likely to make mistakes. Because of loss of muscle power and control, reduced attention span, slowdown of reactions, and loss of sensitivity, you become more susceptible to injury.

Exhausted legs may tremble and fail to operate brakes promptly. A slight stumble may become a major fall. And a load that you could normally lift may be too much for you to control.

This Could Be You...Mario felt he could put in a fence in his sleep, which was a good thing because he almost felt like he was asleep. This was his sixth 12-hour day in a row, and he was beat. But the job was just about finished. Just a dozen more posts to set. Mario had the posts on a trailer, and he couldn't believe how heavy this last batch felt. Normally he could hoist two posts at a time, but now it was all he could do to control one. Maybe that's why he didn't notice how unstable the pile of posts was. He was jerking on one post, trying to get it free, when suddenly the whole pile started moving. Before he could react, he was on the ground with half a dozen posts lying on his legs and chest. Mario hoped the sharp pain in his ankle was just a sprain.

To avoid general muscle fatigue, rest regularly. Frequent short pauses are more effective than longer rests at wider intervals. Take rests in the late morning and late afternoon. Also, eating nutritious food (i.e. fruit, vegetables, fruit juice, and crackers) throughout the day will help maintain strength and prevent fatigue.

TOBACCO, DRUGS, AND ALCOHOL

Some people like to think they are exceptions to the rule. That drugs or stimulants or depressants don't really affect their ability to perform. However, all these substances definitely have effects on your personal capabilities and limitations.

Tobacco

The long-term effects of tobacco use are well documented. But smoking also affects you and your work performance in the short term. Smoking reduces work capacity as much as 10 percent because of carbon monoxide (CO) in a smoker's blood. Tobacco smoke contains carbon monoxide and the blood absorbs that CO. This reduces the oxygen carrying capacity of the blood; thus making a smoker short winded. Fatigue will set in quicker, making the smoker more likely to make the miscalculations typical of fatigued workers.

Alcohol

Any amount of alcohol in the blood affects human coordination and reflexes. As the amount of alcohol in the blood goes up, performance goes down and reactions get slower. Never mix alcohol and outdoor power equipment. Using outdoor power equipment requires an alert operator in full command of his or her abilities.

Drugs

When we talk about drugs, we mean everything from aspirin to heroin. And while few would argue the bad effects of illegal drugs on your body, it's important to remember that all drugs have some chemical effect on you.

Even perfectly safe over-the-counter medications can interfere with your ability to work effectively. Some cold medications can make you drowsy or feel disconnected. Pain relievers may relieve muscle aches caused by illness or overexertion, but this lack of pain does not mean you've regained all your strength.

This doesn't mean you can't work if you take medications. What it does mean (once again) is that you need to be aware of your limitations. Don't smoke, don't take illegal drugs, and with any medication read the label and understand any side effects.

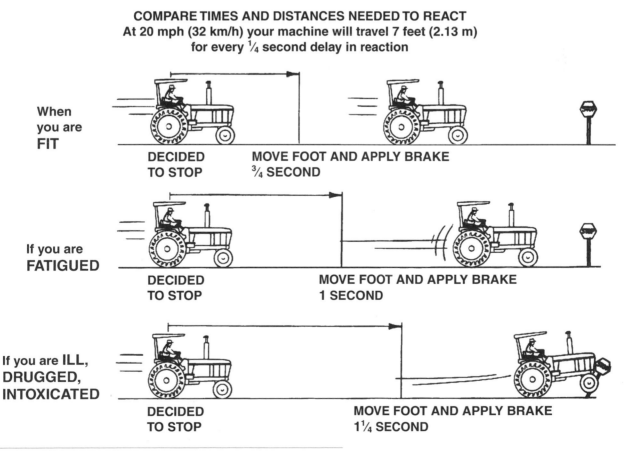

COMPARE TIMES AND DISTANCES NEEDED TO REACT
At 20 mph (32 km/h) your machine will travel 7 feet (2.13 m)
for every ¼ second delay in reaction

When you are **FIT**
DECIDED TO STOP
MOVE FOOT AND APPLY BRAKE ¾ SECOND

If you are **FATIGUED**
DECIDED TO STOP
MOVE FOOT AND APPLY BRAKE 1 SECOND

If you are **ILL, DRUGGED, INTOXICATED**
DECIDED TO STOP
MOVE FOOT AND APPLY BRAKE 1¼ SECOND

Fig. 6 – Fatigue, Illness, Alcohol, Drugs and Medicine affect Reaction Time

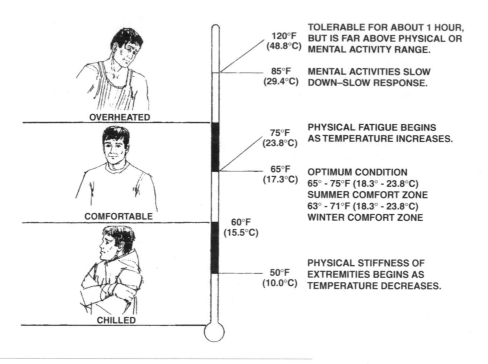

120°F (48.8°C)	TOLERABLE FOR ABOUT 1 HOUR, BUT IS FAR ABOVE PHYSICAL OR MENTAL ACTIVITY RANGE.
85°F (29.4°C)	MENTAL ACTIVITIES SLOW DOWN–SLOW RESPONSE.
75°F (23.8°C)	PHYSICAL FATIGUE BEGINS AS TEMPERATURE INCREASES.
65°F (17.3°C)	OPTIMUM CONDITION 65° - 75°F (18.3° - 23.8°C) SUMMER COMFORT ZONE 63° - 71°F (18.3° - 23.8°C) WINTER COMFORT ZONE
60°F (15.5°C)	
50°F (10.0°C)	PHYSICAL STIFFNESS OF EXTREMITIES BEGINS AS TEMPERATURE DECREASES.

OVERHEATED

COMFORTABLE

CHILLED

Fig. 7 – Temperature and Humidity Affect your Comfort and Work Performance

ENVIRONMENTAL CONDITIONS

Common environmental factors that affect landscape and golf course workers are:

- **temperature and humidity**
- **vibration**
- **noise**
- **dust and mold.**

COLD

It's hard to be a productive worker when you are too hot or too cold. And while you can't do much about the weather, you can do a lot to limit how the weather affects your body.

If you are working in cold conditions, you obviously need to dress warm. But there's more than one way to dress warm. You need to select clothing that's right for the job you will be doing.

Heavy, bulky clothes such as a snowmobile suit are OK if you are basically sitting or standing in one place for long periods of time, directing traffic for example.

But this bulky kind of clothing possesses several problems if you are going to be active out in the cold. It can restrict your freedom of movement, making you clumsier on the job. Plus these heavy garments are difficult to ventilate. When you perspire, moisture can be trapped inside, causing you to actually chill more easily.

The best cold-weather wear, especially for the active worker, is layers of clothing. With layers you can customize what you wear to the outside temperature and your activity. These layers might include a jacket over a sweater over a shirt over an undershirt. If you are very active, you may need to remove the jacket or sweater to keep from overheating. If your task becomes less strenuous, you may put the sweater and/or jacket back on. Wearing a hat and/or hood will make your whole body feel warmer.

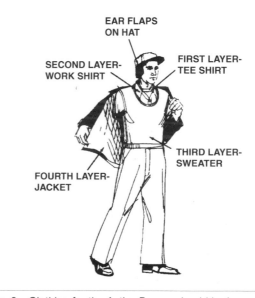

EAR FLAPS ON HAT

SECOND LAYER-WORK SHIRT

FIRST LAYER-TEE SHIRT

THIRD LAYER-SWEATER

FOURTH LAYER-JACKET

Fig. 8 – Clothing for the Active Person should be Layered.

Avoid wearing cotton next to your skin in cold weather. It absorbs and holds your perspiration giving you a cold, wet chill. Wool, silk, and some synthetic materials like polyester fleece and polypropylene stay dry, even as you sweat. These fabrics stay dry by moving (or wicking) perspiration away from your skin. Keeping that first layer of clothing dry will go a long way to keeping you warm.

What you eat can also help keep you warm. A high-calorie, high-protein diet is required to give a person enough energy to work and keep warm in cold weather.

HEAT

Working in hot, humid conditions poses greater challenges. Water is very important for the body to adjust to high temperatures. In order to keep body temperature normal; you need to drink enough water to equal the rate of water loss from perspiration and other body functions. So when it's hot, you need to drink plenty of water. Doctors recommend typical office workers drink 64 ounces of water each day. If you are working up a sweat outside, you should drink much more water than that.

Fig. 9 – Drink Plenty of Water

High humidity poses additional problems. If both temperature and humidity are high, perspiration can't evaporate, and the body quickly becomes overheated. You normally cannot continue working when your body temperature exceeds 102 degrees F. (39 degrees C.).

Here are some tips to keep you working comfortably and safely in hot weather.

1. **Dress for hot weather**. Lightweight, light-colored clothing reflects heat and sunlight. Cotton breathes better and is thus cooler than polyester clothing. (A switch from our cold-weather advice.)

2. **Drink plenty of water.** Hot weather can wring you out before you know it. Make sure you don't dehydrate.

3. **Eat carbohydrates.** (pasta, rice, potatoes, breads) Avoid foods high in fat. Digesting fat produces higher body heat than carbohydrates. Proteins increase water loss.

4. **Get needed potassium.** If you are sweating you need foods and liquids that are good sources of potassium and sodium (unless a restricted diet prevents it). Most fruits and fruit juices are rich in potassium. Crackers and pretzels are good sources of sodium.

5. **Slow down in hot weather**. Your body works harder when temperature and humidity are high. That means you need to take it easier.

6. **Heed the early warnings of heat stress.** Watch out for headache, heavy perspiration, high pulse rate, and shallow breathing. Take a break and get to a cooler place.

7. **Find a cool place to work.** If you can work in a place that's shady or windy you will be less affected by the heat. If possible, arrange your tasks so you can be in the shade during the hottest part of the day.

8. **Avoid thermal shock.** Get used to warmer weather gradually. Take it easy those first two or three hot days. Your body will probably adjust if you take it slow.

9. **Don't get too much sun**. Sunburn makes the job of keeping cool much more difficult. Ultraviolet rays of the sun also cause skin cancer. (See next section.)

THE SUN AND SKIN CANCER

Because they spend so much time out in the sun, landscape and golf course workers should take precautions to prevent skin cancer. Skin cancer is a serious disease. According to the American Cancer Institute more than 800,000 people in the United States are treated for skin cancer each year. Close to 10,000 people die from skin cancer every year.

The most common cause of skin cancer is overexposure to the sun. Research has found that a major factor in the development of all skin cancers is not one or two bad sunburns, but rather the combined effect of repeated exposure to the sun. Each time human skin is exposed to sunlight; there are minute changes in the layers of the skin. Add up lots of exposures to the sun, and the chance of skin cancer increases.

ASYMMETRY – ONE HALF UNLIKE THE OTHER HALF.

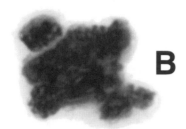

BORDER IRREGULAR – SCALLOPED OR POORLY CIRCUMSCRIBED BORDER.

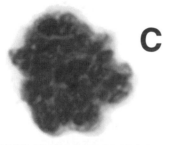

COLOR VARIED FROM ONE AREA TO ANOTHER; SHADES OF TAN AND BROWN; BLACK; SOMETIMES WHITE, RED OR BLUE.

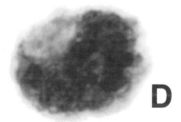

DIAMETER LARGER THAN 6MM AS A RULE (DIAMETER OF A PENCIL ERASER).

Fig. 9A – ABCDs of Melanoma Detection. Look for Danger Signs in Pigmented Lesions of the Skin. Consult Your Dermatologist Immediately if Any of Your Moles or Pigmented Spots Exhibit Any of These Characteristics

People most at risk are those who burn easily, rarely tan, and have a fair complexion with blond or red hair, or blue or gray eyes. But don't think you're in the clear if you have dark hair or dark skin. The sun causes skin damage even in those not in the highest-risk group.

PREVENT SKIN CANCER FROM SUN

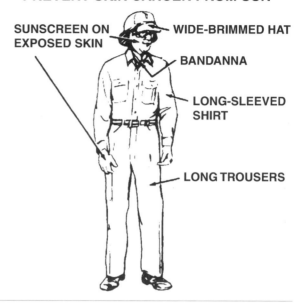

Fig. 10 – Protective Clothing and Sunscreen Help Prevent Skin Cancer

There are several things you can do to protect your skin from sun damage. If possible, avoid skin exposure to the sun during the midday hours of 10 a.m. to 3 p.m. These are the hours when the sun's rays are most direct and cause the most damage.

For many people it's impossible to avoid the sun during those hours. If that's your situation, protect your skin with clothing, or by applying sunscreen.

Clothing is the more effective protection. Wear long pants and long-sleeve shirts. Wear gloves to protect your hands. Do this year around. The sun can cause skin damage in every season.

Headgear is also important. The best headwear provides sun protection for the face, ears, and back of the neck—which means wide-brimmed hats or caps with a rear flap attached. Note the popular baseball-style caps provide no protection for ear tips and the back of the neck, which are common locations for skin cancer on people who work outside.

Fig. 11 – Wear Sun-safe Hats that Protect your Ears, Neck and Face

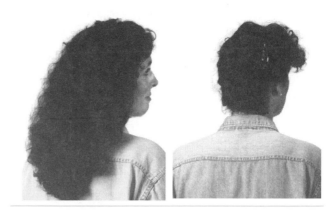

Fig. 12 – Long Hair should be Pulled Tightly away from your Face and Neck

Use sunscreen with a sun protection factor (SPF) of at least 15. The more you are outdoors and the more you sweat, the more you'll need to reapply it. If you have extremely sensitive skin, or your skin is already sunburned, use sunblock. When properly applied it offers protection and will prevent further skin damage.

To protect your eyes from sun-induced cataracts and other damage, wear sunglasses with an ultraviolet (UV) rating of 100. Look for the words "blockage" or "absorption" on the label rather than just "protection".

DRESSING SAFELY

Clothing not only protects you from the sun; it can also protect you from some equipment-related hazards. Lawn mowers, line trimmers, and some other outdoor power equipment can send rocks and chunks of wood flying at high speeds. In these kinds of conditions you don't want to be wearing shorts and a tank top. Instead, you'll want to wear sturdy, long work pants and a long-sleeve shirt.

Make sure your clothes fit snugly. Baggy pants and shirts are more likely to get caught in equipment.

Long hair should be pulled tightly away from your face and neck then secured firmly and covered with a snug hat. Do not wear ponytails or long braids, they can catch on turning shafts or drives with disastrous results. People have been scalped by getting long hair tangled in turning machine parts.

Never wear clothes with loose straps, dangling strings, or big rips. Remove drawstrings from jackets and sweatshirts. Any of these items can catch and wrap on a turning shaft, pulling you into the machine. Shirt tails, flowing scarves, dangling jewelry, and long hair that is not tied up are dangerous.

Proper footwear is important for both protection of your toes and sure footing. As a general rule, wear heavy-duty, closed-toe shoes with good traction soles. That means no athletic shoes and no sandals.

When working with most outdoor power equipment you should wear eye and ear protection. Regular prescription glasses and stereo headphones do not offer protection. In fact, stereo headphones are worse than no hearing protection. The music can distract you from your job, the dangling wires can get tangled in the equipment, and if the stereo is set to play louder than the equipment you are running, it may cause hearing damage.

Proper clothing required for the task will vary depending on the machine you operate. Read the operator's manual for its advice on proper attire.

DO WEAR RECOMMENDED HEAD, EYE, AND HEARING PROTECTION.

DO WEAR SUN-SAFE HATS THAT PROTECT YOUR EARS AND NECK AS WELL AS YOUR FACE.

DO WEAR CLOTHING THAT FITS RIGHT AND IS IN GOOD CONDITION. FRAYED AND RAGGED EDGES ARE DANGEROUS.

DO REMOVE JEWELRY BEFORE GOING TO WORK.

DO WEAR JACKETS AND SWEATSHIRTS THAT ARE PROPERLY SIZED AND DO NOT HAVE DRAWSTRINGS.

DO WEAR CLOSE-FITTING PULLOVERS

DO WEAR GLOVES THAT FIT WELL, PROVIDE GOOD GRIP, AND ARE IN GOOD CONDITION.

DO WEAR JEANS THAT ARE THE RIGHT LENGTH. CUFFS CAN BE DANGEROUS.

DO CHOOSE CLOTHING WITH BANDED CUFFS. AVOID CUFFS THAT NEED BUTTONING.

DO WEAR STURDY BOOTS WITH GOOD SLIP-RESITANT TREAD.

DO KEEP SHOELACES SHORT OR TUCK THEM INTO YOUR SHOES.

Fig. 13 – The "Do's" of Proper Dressing

Do wear sturdy boots with good slip-resistant tread.

Do wear jeans that are the right length. Cuffs can be dangerous.

Do wear close-fitting pullovers.

Do wear gloves that fit well, provide good grip, and are in good condition.

Do wear clothing that fits right and is in good condition. Frayed and ragged edges are dangerous.

Do wear recommended protective equipment for head, eye, and hearing protection.

Do wear sun-safe hats that protect your ears and neck as well as your face.

Do remove jewelry before going to work.

Do wear jackets and sweatshirts that are properly sized and do not have drawstrings.

Do choose clothing with banded cuffs. Avoid cuffs that need buttoning.

Do keep shoelaces short or tuck them into your shoes.

DON'T GO OUTSIDE WITHOUT PROPER HEADWEAR.

DON'T WEAR JEWELRY OR USE PORTABLE RADIOS.

DON'T WEAR CLOTHING WITH DRAWSTRINGS OR HOODS.

DON'T WEAR JACKETS OPEN! INSTEAD ZIP UP, BUTTON UP, OR BETTER YET USE A CLOSE-FITTED PULLOVER.

DON'T WEAR GLOVES THAT ARE TOO BIG.

DON'T WEAR LOOSE OR ILL-FITTING CLOTHES.

DON'T WEAR FRAYED PANTS OR SHIRTS.

DON'T WEAR LIGHTWEIGHT SHOES OR SHOES WITH LACES THAT ARE TOO LONG.

DON'T CUFF SHIRTS OR PANTS— BUY THEM TO FIT INSTEAD.

Fig. 14 – The "Don't's" of Proper Dressing

Don't cuff shirts or pants—buy them to fit instead.

Don't wear jackets open! Instead zip up, button up, or better yet use a close-fitted pullover.

Don't wear frayed pants or shirts.

Don't wear loose or ill-fitting clothes.

Don't go outside without proper headwear.

Don't wear jewelry or use portable radios.

Don't wear gloves that are too big.

Don't wear clothing with drawstrings or hoods.

Don't wear lightweight shoes or shoes with laces that are too long.

PERSONAL PROTECTIVE EQUIPMENT

For many landscape and golf course jobs you need more protection than just good work clothes can provide. What you need is personal protective equipment or PPE as safety experts call it.

In this section we'll discuss different PPE devices that protect the:

- **head**
- **eyes**
- **ears**
- **hands**
- **respiratory system**

HEAD PROTECTION

The most effective head protection is a hard hat. It protects against bumps and falling objects. Some hard hats have warm liners for cold-weather work. Use hard hats for building work, trimming trees, or other jobs where falling objects could cause head injuries. Lightweight bump caps are intended only to protect against bumping your head against objects. They are not a substitute to be worn as hard hats – they do not protect from falling objects. Approved hard hats are identified by the ANSI Z89.1 code.

HARD HAT   **BUMP CAP**

Fig. 15 – Head Protection

What is an ANSI code?

ANSI stands for the American National Standards Institute. It is a non-profit, membership organization that helps develop design and performance standards for a wide variety of businesses and technologies. These standards are much like rules that manufacturers agree to follow. With eye protection, for example, if a pair of safety glasses meets the ANSI standard, you know it is made of special impact-resistant materials that can withstand a high level of shock. If you buy eye protection that doesn't meet the ANSI standard, you are left to guess how much protection you really have.

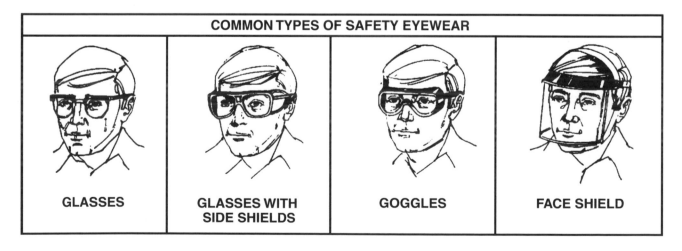

COMMON TYPES OF SAFETY EYEWEAR			
GLASSES	**GLASSES WITH SIDE SHIELDS**	**GOGGLES**	**FACE SHIELD**

Fig. 16 – Common Types of Safety Eyewear

EYE PROTECTION

Eyes are very sensitive and need protection from flying objects, chemicals, dust, and chaff. You should wear eye protection whenever you are working in a shop, spraying paint, applying chemicals, or working in dusty conditions. If you are using outdoor power equipment, it's generally a good idea to wear eye protection. Check the machine's operator's manual for the manufacturer's recommendation. Approved eye protection will be marked with the ANSI Z87.1 coding.

There are several types of protective devices for your eyes (Fig. 16).

If you wear eyeglasses or sunglasses for work, be sure they have impact-resistant lenses. The lenses of approved safety glasses are made of special impact-resistant materials so they withstand more shock than ordinary lenses. Side shields can be added to glasses to guard against flying particles coming from the side.

Goggles protect the eyes from impact of flying objects from the front and sides. Some goggles have vents to limit perspiration buildup and fogging of the lenses. Unvented goggles provide protection against chemical vapors and liquids.

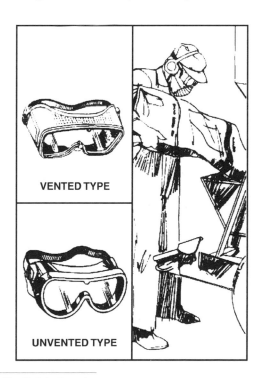

VENTED TYPE

UNVENTED TYPE

Fig. 17 – Safety Goggles

Face shields protect the face from splashing, dust, and chaff, but they provide very little protection against impact. If you need protection from flying objects, wear safety glasses or goggles under the shield or get a special impact-resistant shield that's fitted to a hard hat.

HEARING PROTECTION

Hearing loss can be a very serious problem for anyone working long hours around outdoor power equipment. If you are exposed to loud noise you should be wearing hearing protection.

But how do you know if your working situation is too loud? The first step is to get an idea of how loud your work environment is. Noise level is measured in decibels. Many people mistakenly assume a few decibels increase is not significant. In fact, every 3 decibels increase in sound represents a doubling of the intensity level This is the sound we feel, and what can damage hearing. Thus 103 decibels is twice the sound intensity of a 100-decibel noise. Here are some decibel levels for common activities:

- **50 gentle breeze, babbling stream**
- **60 normal conversation**
- **85 idling tractor**
- **90 full-throttle lawn mower, passing motorcycle**
- **100 working tractor, table saw**
- **110 snowblower, average personal stereo with earphones set at mid volume**
- **120 old chain saw, tractor with bad muffler, thunder clap**

The danger of hearing loss gets serious at about 85 decibels. Anytime you have to shout to be heard by someone standing three feet away, the noise level is probably greater than 85 decibels.

Hearing damage generally does not come from hearing one loud sound. Rather it is the effect of hearing loud noises over a period of the time. The louder the noise the less time it takes to cause damage.

At 90 decibels noise may begin to affect your hearing if you're exposed to it for more than eight hours per day. As noise gets louder, the "safe" time decreases. At 95 decibels hearing damage can occur if you're exposed more than four hours per day. One hour of noise at 105 decibels can cause hearing damage, while exposure to just 15 minutes per day of 115 decibels can cause hearing damage.

Here are other guidelines to identify work situations that are causing hearing damage:

- **Your ears ring after you are exposed to the noise.**
- **Speech and other sounds are muffled after you are exposed to the noise.**
- **While working you have to shout to be heard by someone next to you.**

There are a variety of products available to protect your hearing, ranging from earplugs to ear muffs. In selecting hearing protection look for the Noise Reduction Rating (NRR) label on the device. The NRR gives an estimate of the hearing protection provided. For example, ear plugs marked "NRR 26" are intended to reduce noise levels 26 decibels.Unfortunately, the rating is for ideal conditions. In actual use it may provide only 50 percent of the rated protection. Thus in a 100-decibel environment, these earplugs would lower the sounds you hear only about 13 decibels. Be sure to use models that have a high enough Noise Reduction Rating for the job you are performing.

EARPLUG

EARMUFFS

Fig. 18 – Foam or Rubber Earplugs (top) or Acoustical Earmuffs (bottom)

While earplugs can provide adequate hearing protection, earmuffs have other advantages. They don't carry dirt into the ear canal. Earmuffs also block more noise than earplugs because they cover the sound-conducting bones around the ears, as well as the ears themselves.

 CAUTION: Safety Alert - Don't use cotton balls to plug your ears. You are not getting hearing protection. Cotton blocks only a few low-frequency sounds and it doesn't block high-frequency sound at all.

HAND PROTECTION

Gloves can't always prevent a serious injury, but they can guard against cuts, abrasions, chemicals, and skin irritations.

Leather gloves protect hands against sharp objects and give good gripping power. Nitrile gloves are recommended if you are working with chemicals. Canvas and cotton gloves provide some protection, but never wear them when working around pesticides. They absorb and trap chemicals, actually increasing your exposure to the pesticide. (For more information on the right gloves for chemical application see Chapter 13.)

Wear gloves that fit snuggly but not too tight. If gloves stretch out, they get thinner and offer less protection. If they are too big they limit your grip and they can more easily get caught in moving parts.

VIBRATION

Many pieces of outdoor power equipment transmit some vibration to their operators. The amount of vibration varies greatly from one type of machine to another. While your body can absorb some vibration with no noticeable side effects, long-term exposure to vibration can cause permanent nerve and muscle damage. One vibration-related ailment that could affect landscapers and golf course workers is called Raynaud's Syndrome.

Raynaud's Syndrome is a disorder of blood circulation to the fingers. This condition is aggravated with exposure to cold. It is important to know the signs and symptoms of Raynaud's Syndrome. Awareness can prevent the disorder from occurring or progressing to a serious stage. If not detected in the early stages, the disorder can permanently impair blood circulation in the fingers.

Typical symptoms of Raynaud's Syndrome include:

- **tingling and slight loss of feeling or numbness in the fingers**
- **whitening of the fingers, usually not affecting the thumb**
- **pain, sometimes with redness, happening 30 minutes to two hours after exposure to cold and/or vibration.**

Here are some ways to limit your chances of being injured by vibration:

- **Keep your body warm, especially the head and neck, hands and wrists, feet and hands.**
- **Wear sturdy gloves to keep your hands warm and absorb some of the vibration.**
- **Make sure machines are properly adjusted. Machines that are not tuned or are out of balance will vibrate more.**
- **Hold vibrating tools as lightly as is necessary to maintain good control. Avoid stiff "death grips" while the unit is working.**
- **Limit the amount of time you spend using hand-held machines that vibrate. Try to fill part of each workday with jobs where vibrating tools are not required.**
- **If tingling, numbness, or other signs of Raynaud's Syndrome develop, promptly consult a physician.**

RESPIRATORY PROTECTION

There are many styles and types of respiratory protection devices. Each is designed for specific situations. Some devices filter out pesticide vapors; some will filter out nuisance dust while others filter out toxic dust. It's important that you choose the correct filter for the task you have at hand. Choosing the wrong device may be the same as having no protection at all.

To help you make the right decision look for the NIOSH (National Institute of Safety and Health) "approval number." The approval number will tell you what applications the device can safely be used for.

The simplest type of protection is the filter mask respirator. These are soft fiber devices that cover the nose and mouth and trap harmful material before it can enter your lungs. There are numerous types of filter mask respirators. Make sure you have one that offers the protection you need.

Understand that some filters are designed for only homeowner use. These low-cost models are not NIOSH certified and not recommended for commercial applications. Again, make sure the filter mask respirator you buy is designed for the situation you face.

Cartridge respirators have a facemask fitted with one or two replaceable cartridges. The cartridges contain an absorbent material (often activated charcoal) that purifies inhaled air. To trap particles, filters can be added in front of the cartridge.

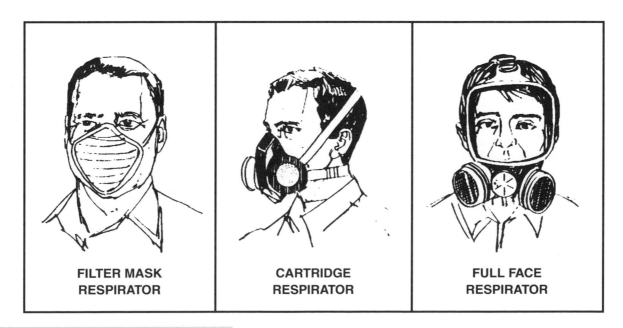

| FILTER MASK RESPIRATOR | CARTRIDGE RESPIRATOR | FULL FACE RESPIRATOR |

Fig. 19 – Choose the Right Respirator for your Task

NO!
WRONG LIFTING POSITION!

PROPER LIFTING POSITION!

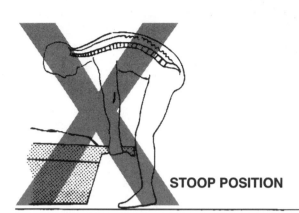

STOOP POSITION

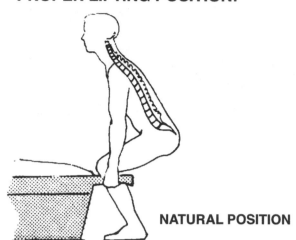

NATURAL POSITION

Fig. 20 – Use the Proper Lifting Position

With cartridge respirators you need to be sure you have the right type of cartridge installed for the contaminant present and its concentration level. Also make sure the cartridge life has not "expired."

Make sure respirators fit snuggly at all face-contact points to prevent chemical vapors from bypassing the filters. Since facial hair makes a snug fit more difficult, respirator users should not have beards.

Also make sure your eyes are adequately protected. In many applications goggles should be worn with the respirator. Some respirators come with built-in, full-face splash protection.

LIFTING

About three-fourths of us will be affected by back disorders sometime during our lives. Back disorders are common, even in the 20-to-30 age group. These ailments often begin with incorrect lifting.

When a person lifts by bending over (what we call the stoop position), a lot of pressure is put on the spine. This leverage can create a force as great as 1,500 pounds (700 kilograms) on your back even when you are lifting only 110 pounds (50 kilograms). This extreme pressure can rupture a disk in your back, sometimes causing permanent injury. The proper lifting position minimizes the pressure on your back.

Use the proper lifting procedures and body position, and you'll greatly reduce the risk of injury.

1. **Get a good footing.** Remove obstacles and debris that could cause a fall. Position your feet slightly apart for better balance.

2. **Bend your knees.** Get close to the object. Keep your back in a natural position. Do not force your back to be abnormally straight or curved.

3. **Get a good grip.** Grasp the object with a full-hand grip instead of your fingertips. It's less likely to slip and fall. Tilt boxes and get one hand under them. Place the other hand diagonally opposite. This principle of gripping diagonally also applies to sacks of fertilizer, seed, etc.

4. **Avoid twisting as you lift.** Twisting or bending sideways increases the risk of injury.

5. **Lift with your leg muscles.** Lift smoothly, not with a jerk. Keep the load close to your body.

6. **Balance the weight.** Carry loads at the center of your body to balance the weight.

7. **Reverse the procedure to set an object down.** Keep your back in a natural position and bend your knees to lower an object.

8. **Get mechanical help.** Use the equipment you have at your disposal. Use a hoist or loader to lift a heavy load from the floor. Don't be laid up for a week or a lifetime with a bad back because you tried to save a few minutes.

Fig. 21 – the Assisted One-hand Lift helps Reduce Stress on the Lower Back

Sometimes a barrier, such as a partition, or the wall of a pickup truck bed will prevent you from using the lift procedures we've discussed. You may be able to use the assisted one-hand lifting method. While you grab the object with one hand, push downward with the other hand as you lift. This helps distribute the stress over the shoulder and arm muscles, thereby reducing stress on the lower back.

SECOND-PARTY MISHAPS

Several times in this chapter we've suggested getting help when you need it. But it's not always safer to have a helper. Whenever there are two people involved, there's the chance that what one person does may injure another. This is especially true if you are working with, or near, outdoor power equipment. These types of incidents are called second party mishaps because they involve a second person.

One of the keys to avoiding second-party mishaps is for each person to know exactly where the other person is and what he or she is going to do. Clear communication is essential. Go over what you want a second party to do and have that second party repeat the instructions back to you. If noise limits your ability to talk to each other while you are working together, agree on hand signals for important directions.

If you are working together on a machine, make all adjustments with the engine shut off and no one on the operator's station. Why is this a big deal? Obviously, with the power shut off, drives can't engage. But even with the power shut off, someone on the operator's station could bump a lever, or release a brake that could have dire consequences.

Before approaching a working machine, signal the operator to stop and shut down the equipment. Approach only after all moving parts have stopped.

Fig. 23 – Signal the Machine Operator and Wait for Everything to Stop Before Approaching

For large equipment that blocks your view, walk completely around the machine before starting it. That way you'll be sure all second parties are clear. Sounding the horn, or yelling, "Starting!" before starting the engine also gives warning to those in the area.

This Could Be You...It was going to be an easy way to move that metal beam. Ed had a log chain attached to the loader bucket. He would simply drive up to the beam, have Joe attach the log chain, and the beam would be up and out of there in no time. Everything was going as planned until Joe called out for "more chain." Unfortunately, Ed thought he said "move chain," and lifted the bucket. Instead of the chain going slack, it went tight, crushing Joe's fingers against the metal beam. Ed heard the painful yell above the drone of the tractor, but by then it was too late. The "easy" move turned into three broken fingers and three hours at the emergency room.

Extra riders are the cause of many second-party mishaps. Here's the rule—no extra riders. If there isn't a second seat, there shouldn't be second rider. Outdoor power equipment is for work. It's not a form of transportation for fellow workers.

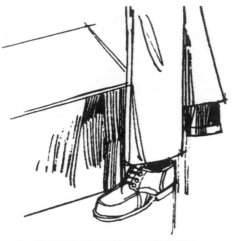

A. STAND CLOSE TO OBJECT TO BE LIFTED

B. BEND THE KNEES

C. TILT THE BOX PLACING ONE HAND UNDER

D. PLACE HAND DIAGONALLY OPPOSITE

E. GET A FULL HAND GRIP— NOT JUST FINGERTIPS

F. LIFT WITH LEGS KEEP BACK NATURAL

Fig. 22 – Practice Proper Lifting Procedures to Avoid Serious Back Injury

It's important to keep others away from working equipment. If you see people or pets stray into the work area, stop the machine until they leave. Never take anyone for a ride on equipment. If there isn't a seat, there shouldn't be a rider.

Fig. 24 – Never Take Extra Riders on Equipment

Ways to Avoid Second-Party Mishaps

- **No extra riders, ever.**

- **Training should be done with an approved instructional seat.**

- **Clearly communicate what each party is going to do before you start a task.**

- **Plan the job so a mistake can't cause an injury.**

- **Walk completely around large machines that limit your visibility to be sure there are no second parties in danger.**

- **Honk the horn or yell, "Starting!" to warn people in the area you are starting the equipment.**

- **If people or pets stray into the work area, stop the machine until they leave.**

- **If you need to talk to someone who is operating a machine, stay a safe distance away until you can get the operator's attention. Approach only after the machine has come to a complete stop.**

ADDITIONAL RESOURCES

Mowing Safety Know-How, Deere & Company, Product Safety Department, Moline, IL 61265-8098

The Do's and Don'ts of Respiratory Protection, Gempler's, P.O. Box 328 Belleville WI 53508, ph. 800-382-8473

American Cancer Society–www.cancer.org

National Farm Medicine Center–www.marshfieldclinic.org/nfmc

TEST YOURSELF

QUESTIONS - CHAPTER 2

1. What is the best way to dress if you'll be working out in cold weather?

2. Name two good ways to protect yourself from skin cancer.

3. How could having a helper actually be a safety hazard?

4. What is PPE?

MACHINE FACTORS

3

INTRODUCTION

Outdoor power equipment is designed to perform specific tasks. These machines use power, motion, and your energy to do these tasks, and as a result they present a number of potential hazards to the operator.

For example, the blade of a lawn mower must rotate at a high speed to cut grass. If an operator comes in contact with the spinning blade, even for an instant, a serious injury will result.

It would be nice if manufacturers could design their products to eliminate all chances of operator injury, but that is just not possible if a machine is to do its job. All potential hazards cannot be eliminated. Lawn mowers, for example, do have shielding to prevent your foot from slipping into the spinning blade, but if the blade were completely covered by shields, it would not be able to cut grass.

Since all hazards cannot be eliminated, it's important to understand common machine hazards. Working safely will require you to understand the potential dangers of any machine you may come in contact with.

SQUEEZE HANDLES TOGETHER

Fig. 1 – Operator-presence Systems (left) and ROPS (Rollover Protective Structure) are Two Examples of Designs that make Outdoor Power Equipment Safer

SAFER MACHINES

While all hazards cannot be eliminated, manufacturers of outdoor power equipment have done many things to make equipment safer. Here are some approaches or strategies used by engineers to design safer machines:

- **Make it easier for the operator to do the right thing.** For example, many self-propelled machines have an operator-presence system that shuts off the engine if the operator gets out of the seat. With walk-behind lawnmowers, the engine and/or blade stop if the operator lets go of the handle.

- **Use shielding to prevent the operator from coming in contact with a hazard.** Power take-off (**PTO**) shafts, for example, have shields that stop turning if contacted, even though the internal shaft continues to turn.

- **Protect the operator.** The rollover protective structure (**ROPS**) on tractors protects the operator (provided the seat belt is worn) if the tractor should roll over.

- **Provide safety instructions.** This safety advice can be in the operator's manual and on warning signs on the equipment.

But good design cannot protect the operator from every hazard, and warning signs and operator's manuals cannot predict every situation that may pose a danger. That's why it's so important to understand common machine hazards.

COMMON MACHINE HAZARDS

Here are some common machine hazards you should understand and be able to recognize:

- pinch points
- wrap points
- shear and cutting points
- crush points
- pull-in points
- freewheeling parts
- thrown objects
- hot surfaces and liquids
- slippery surfaces
- stored energy.

PINCH POINTS

Pinch points are where two parts move together and at least one of them moves in a circle. Pinch points are commonly found in power transmission devices such as belt drives, chain drives, and gear drives.

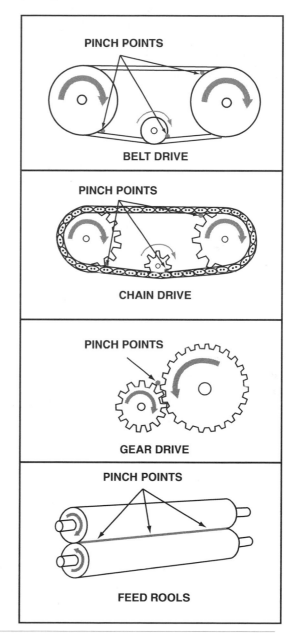

Fig. 2 – Pinch Points on Rotating Parts can Catch Clothing, Hands, Arms, and Feet

Injuries happen when you brush up against unshielded rotating parts or slip and fall against them. Loose clothing, long hair, or jacket drawstrings can get caught in pinch points, pulling you into the moving parts.

Usually outdoor power equipment operates too fast for persons to withdraw from a pinch point once they are caught.

Avoiding Pinch-Point Injuries

It's important to identify pinch points on equipment and keep hands and clothes away. Generally, manufacturers shield pinch points to protect the operator. Always replace shields if you must remove them to repair or adjust a machine. Make sure equipment is shut off and stopped before attempting any adjustments.

If a shield is damaged and no longer useful, contact your equipment dealer for a replacement shield.

This Could Be You...Sam couldn't believe his luck. Friday afternoon, one more client to go, and the drive belt on the mower deck had to break. He gave the mower a good kick. At least he had an old belt in the truck that might work. But there was more bad luck. His kick had bent the shield covering the belt area, and he could hardly get it off. Sam threw the damaged shield into the truck, hoping to get someone at the shop to straighten it before Monday morning came. After 15 minutes the "new" belt was on and he was mowing again. Maybe he'd get done on time after all. Then came the squeal of a slipping belt. Sam leaned over to get a better look. In an instant, he felt a hard tug on his jacket. The exposed belt and pulley had grabbed the lower drawstring of his jacket! As Sam felt himself being jerked down toward the mower, he lost his grip of the mower handles. In an instant, the operator-presence system shut off the engine. The whole incident lasted just a second or two, and other than a mangled jacket and big scare, Sam was all right. Maybe his luck wasn't so bad after all.

WRAP POINTS

Any exposed component that rotates is a potential wrap point. Rotating shafts are the culprits in most wrap-point injuries. Often, the wrapping begins with just a thread or frayed piece of cloth catching on a rotating part. In an instant, the victim is entangled with little chance to escape injury. More fibers wrap around the shaft, and in a split second you can be pulled into the machine.

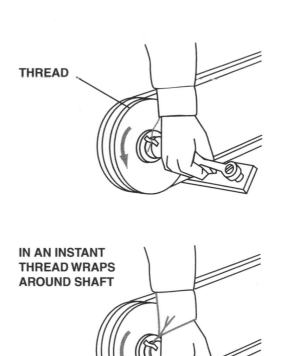

THREAD

IN AN INSTANT THREAD WRAPS AROUND SHAFT

SLEEVE IS IMMEDIATELY PULLED AND BEGINS TO WRAP

Fig. 3 – Wrapping may begin with Just a Thread

You might think you could out pull a few threads, but the more you pull the tighter the wrap. Unless the clothing is very flimsy, you will be dragged in.

Anything dangling from you or your clothes can pull you in— jewelry, long hair, a scarf, jacket fringe, or a loose thread. When working with or near, outdoor power equipment, you should wear close-fitting clothes, avoid jackets with drawstrings, keep long hair tied up above the shoulder, and never wear long, dangly jewelry. (For more information on safe work clothes, see Chapter 2.)

Certain turning components pose special problems. Ends of shafts that protrude beyond bearings can wrap up clothing. Splined, square, and hexagon-shaped shafts are more likely to wrap than smooth shafts. Couplers, universal joints, keys, keyways, pins, and other connecting devices can also wrap clothing.

AGGRESSIVE SHAFTS

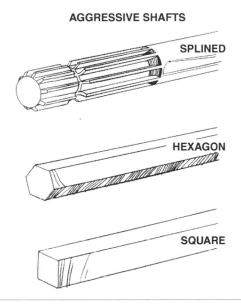

Fig. 4 – Some Shafts are more Aggressive - Thus more likely to Catch and Entangle Things

Smooth shafts often appear harmless, but they too can wrap and wind clothing. Rust, nicks, and dried mud can make them rough enough to catch clothing. Even shafts that rotate slowly must be regarded as potential wrapping points.

SMOOTH SHAFTS CAN BE DANGEROUS BECAUSE OF:

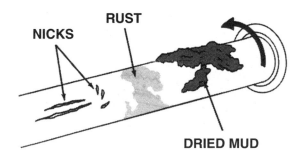

Fig. 5 – Even Shafts that look Smooth can Catch and Wrap Clothing

Avoiding Wrap-Point Mishaps

The best protection against wrap-point hazards is to be aware of them and understand how you can become entangled. Follow these safe practices:

- **Be sure to keep all shields in place and in good working condition.**
- **Wear snug-fitting clothing without frayed edges or drawstrings.**
- **Wear fairly close-cut hair, or securely put your hair up above the shoulder.**
- **Shut off machines before repairing or servicing.**
- **Stay away from unshielded rotating parts.**
- **Use only the proper replacement bolts, pins, or keys on rotating parts. Replacements that are too long or large can increase the potential for wrapping mishaps.**

SHEAR AND CUTTING POINTS

Shear points exist when the edges of two parts move across one another like the blades on shears. Machines such as hedge trimmers and reel mowers have many shear points.

Not all shear points are designed to shear. Frame members that move when an attachment is raised can also have shear points, as can a snowblower discharge. These points are not designed to shear, but they will have that effect on a hand or finger.

Cutting points are similar to shear points in the hazard that they present. Cutting points come from a single object moving rapidly enough to cut a relatively soft object. A rotary lawn mower is a good example. Its single blade shears off the grass by rotating at a high speed.

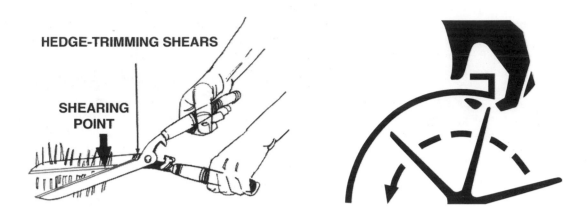

HEDGE-TRIMMING SHEARS

SHEARING
POINT

Fig. 6 – Shear Points can be Two Objects Moving Closely Toward or Across One Another, or One Object moving Near a Stationary Object

Avoiding Shear and Cutting Points

Shearing and cutting devices show no mercy when it comes to limbs, fingers, or toes. A machine can't tell if your fingers or toes are in the wrong place. Since it can't think, you had better.

- **Check over a machine and note all shear points.**
- **Heed all warning signs.**
- **Read the operator's manual. Pay special attention to the safety information.**

Don't count on your reactions to save you. A typical lawn mower blade will make 50 cuts in just half a second. Outdoor power equipment moves faster than you can react.

This Could Be You...It's been 20 years since Nolan lost much of his right index finger, but he remembers it all like it was just yesterday. He was trying to line up some holes so he could mount a loader onto a tractor. One hole was on the loader, the other two on the mounting arm attached to the tractor. Once the holes were lined up, he could easily slide in a mounting pin and the loader would be attached. The holes looked lined up, but the pin would go only in a third of the way. It was an instinctive reaction. Nolan stuck his finger into the hole to feel where the pin was binding. Suddenly the loader slid slightly and the loader arm dropped about 4 inches. Immediately he jerked backed his hand, but most of his finger had already been sheared off. All Nolan could do was stare at his bloody knuckle.

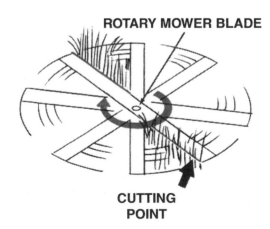

ROTARY MOWER BLADE

CUTTING
POINT

Fig. 7 – Cutting Points Exist when a Sharp Part Moves with Enough Force to Cut Softer Material

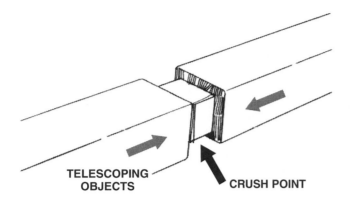

TELESCOPING
OBJECTS

CRUSH POINT

Fig. 8 – Two Kinds of Crush Points: Two Objects Moving Toward Each Other or One Object Moves Toward a Stationary Object

CRUSH POINTS

Crush points exist when two objects move toward each other or when one object moves toward a stationary object. Typical situations that can lead to crush-point injuries include a tractor backing up to an implement or attachment, a machine left in the raised position, or a falling tree.

Avoiding Crush-Point Injuries

Do two things to avoid being crushed:

- **Recognize all potential crush situations.**
- **Stay clear of the hazards.**

This advice may seem simple and obvious. But many people are killed and injured because they get into a crush point. Be constantly alert. Block all equipment securely if you must work under it. Make sure transport or safety locks are in place before going under raised equipment. If an implement can roll, block the wheels so it will stay put.

When two people work together to hitch implements, make sure both are aware of the danger. Each should know what the other person is doing at all times. No one should stand in a crush-point area.

For example, when hooking a 3-point attachment to a tractor, the helper should stand aside while the driver backs up and aligns the attachment. Only after the driver has shut off the engine and set the brakes should the helper step in to make the final attachments.

PULL-IN POINTS

Pull-in injuries often happen when someone attempts to remove material on or near a rotating part of a machine. For example, you may attempt to remove a piece of twine wrapped loosely around a rotating shaft on a rotary-tine tiller. As you pull, it may wrap more tightly. Instead of you pulling the material free, the rotating shaft actually pulls you into the machine (Fig. 9).

Can't you just let go of the twine? That sounds good in theory, but depending upon how fast the shaft is turning, it may pull your hand in before you can react to release your grip.

WHEN PULLING WRAPPED MATERIAL FROM A ROTATING SHAFT, THE MATERIAL MAY TIGHTEN ITS GRIP ON THE SHAFT AND PULL YOU INTO THE MACHINE

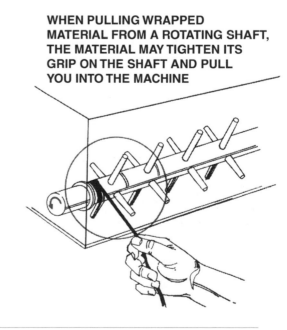

Fig. 9 – Pulling Wrapped Material from a Rotating Shaft

Consider this example of twine loosely wrapped around the shaft of a garden tiller. At full throttle the garden tiller turns at about 200 rpms. If the twine is pulled tight, it will be wrapped onto the shaft at the rate of about 20 inches per second. With a 2-foot piece of twine, your hand would be pulled into the spinning tines in less than a second, hardly enough time to realize the danger and let go of the twine.

Avoiding Pull-In Injuries

You can't have a pull-in injury if something isn't turning. That means you must always shut off the engine and wait for all parts to stop turning before you try to clean, lubricate, or unplug a machine.

Here are some rules to live by:

- **Recognize the potential hazards.**

- **Realize that you can't win speed contests with power equipment.**

- **Keep hands away from all moving parts.**

- **Shut off the machine and wait for all parts to stop before attempting any adjustments.**

FREEWHEELING PARTS

Sometimes parts continue to move after power is shut off. This is "freewheeling." For example, the blade on an edger may continue to spin after the engine has stopped. Likewise, the grinding wheels on a stationary grinder will turn long after its electric motor is shut off. The heavier a part or component and the faster it moves, the longer it will freewheel. If your hand or foot comes in contact with a freewheeling part, your injury may be just as serious as if the power was still on.

Why do people get injured by freewheeling mechanisms?

Here's what victims tell us:

- **They concentrated on the power source, thinking if the power has shut down, the danger is gone.**

- **They underestimated the amount of stored energy in a freewheeling object, thinking they could easily stop the movement.**

- **They thought only about fixing the problem and forgot parts were still moving.**

- **They got impatient and just couldn't wait for all motion to stop.**

Even though an object is moving slowly, it can still cause injury. Objects in motion stay in motion until they are stopped by some other force or object. Don't let your hand or foot be the object that stops a freewheeling part.

Avoiding Freewheeling Injuries

- **Become familiar with the equipment and understand what parts will freewheel after the engine is shut off.**

- **Listen. Most freewheeling parts make some noise.**

- **Watch for signs of motion, even after the engine is shut off.**

- **Never work while using stereo headphones. They can distract you, and keep you from hearing the equipment.**

THROWN OBJECTS

Some outdoor power equipment, such as lawnmowers, rotary cutters, and snowblowers are designed to discharge lots of material. But in some working conditions grass or snow is not the only thing discharged. Stones or chunks of branches can be shot out of the discharge area at high speeds or can ricochet and bounce up causing serious injury. This creates a serious potential hazard, especially to second parties and pets that may be in the work area.

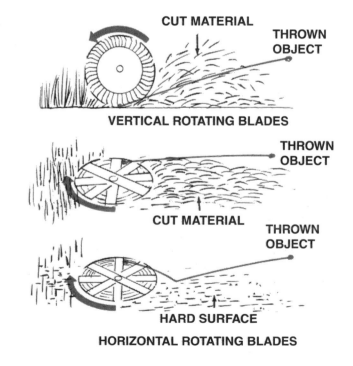

Fig. 10 – Sticks and Stones are Thrown Farther than Grass or Weeds

For example, the typical lawn mower blade spins at 3,000 revolutions per minute. The speed of the blade tip can approach 200 miles per hour. Plus, the blades are shaped to create a vacuuming action to stand the grass up for a cleaner cut. Because of this, the blade can pick up debris like small rocks, broken glass, or sticks, and throw it out the discharge port with considerable force. A harmless-looking stick can become dozens of hurling projectiles.

You know how a flat stone can skip on water. In a similar manner, some machines, such as mowers or rotary cutters, can cause rocks or other objects to ricochet off the ground and upward toward a person. Be careful! Don't assume shields will prevent all thrown-object hazards.

Avoiding Thrown-Object Injuries
Recognize which machines can throw objects.

- **Read the operator's manual to see if eye protection is recommended.**

- **Keep all shields in place to reduce the possibility of thrown objects**

- **Keep people and pets a safe distance away.**

- **Shut off power if anyone approaches the work area.**

- **If practical, clear the work area of objects that might get thrown. For example, pick up fallen branches and debris before mowing a lawn**

WARNING DECALS

Every time you see this symbol ⚠ —the safety alert symbol—your equipment is trying to tell you something. You'll find the symbol on machines and in the operator's manual to alert you to the potential for personal injury.

Following the safety alert symbol, you may find a signal word that identifies a hazard. The three signal words are DANGER, WARNING, and CAUTION.

DANGER warns of the most serious hazards. **WARNING** identifies hazards somewhat serious. **DANGER** or **WARNING** safety signs are located near specific hazards. General precautions are listed on **CAUTION** safety signs.

Carefully read all safety messages in your operator's manual and on your machine. Keep these safety signs in good condition. Replace missing or damaged signs. Keeping safety messages readable could prevent a serious injury. Replacement safety signs are available from your equipment dealer.

HOT SURFACES AND LIQUIDS
Internal combustion engines generate heat. Lots of heat. Coolant temperatures can be over 100 °C (212 °F), and exhaust gasses can heat the outside of a muffler to 500 °C (900 °F). Any of these temperatures can cause serious injury.

To prevent that injury, your first task is to know which surfaces pose the hazards. Look over the machine you are to operate and understand where the exhaust comes out and which related surfaces are hot. These surfaces may or may not be so labeled.

Fig. 12 – Never Check Coolant with the Engine Running

Fig. 11 – Pay Special Attention to Safety Alert Symbols and Signal Words that Follow

You should also understand your machine's cooling system. If it is liquid cooled, understand the dangers of hot, pressurized coolant. Never check the coolant with the engine running. Shut off the engine, and loosen the radiator cap, or radiator expansion-tank cap to the first stop to relieve pressure. Only after all pressure has been released can the cap be removed completely. If possible, wait until everything has cooled down before removing the radiator cap.

If your machine has a hydraulic system, its fluid and components can also become very hot. Understand the location of those hydraulic components and beware of the dangers of hot hydraulic fluid. Let the hydraulic system cool before changing hydraulic filters or removing fittings. Hot oil can severely burn you.

To avoid injures from hot surfaces and liquids follow these safety tips:

- **Understand what parts of your machine are hot. Make sure you know the location of the muffler.**

- **With liquid-cooled engines, release coolant pressure slowly. Better yet, wait until the engine has cooled.**

- **Remember hydraulic fluid on working equipment can be very hot.**

- **Let the engine cool before changing engine oil, radiator coolant, or hydraulic fluid.**

This Could Be You...Tameka had hoped to catch her supervisor before he left for lunch. But as she approached the service building, she could see him heading toward his car. She thought she could still catch him. When she reached the parking lot, she threw the tractor out of gear, hit the brakes, and though it was still coasting a little, she started to jump off. That's when her right foot caught the log chain that was curled up on the tractor platform. Tameka lost her balance and ended up falling right in front of the still-coasting tractor. The rear tire rolled onto her ankle and came to a stop. It would be 45 minutes before anyone realized that she was pinned under the tractor.

SLIPPERY SURFACES

Except for the very frail, slips and falls may not seem like a very important safety issue. But according to reports from the National Safety Council, slips and falls are among the most frequent personal-injury incidents around homes and work sites.

Working around power equipment adds an extra level of danger to a slip or fall. When you slip, you may end up falling onto or under the machine you're using. This could turn a simple fall into a fatal mishap.

Tractors and self-propelled power equipment have steps, handholds, ladders, or platforms to help you get on and off safely. Always use these deliberately, facing the machine when getting on or off.

Fig. 13 – Face the Tractor and Use Stops and Handholds when getting On or Off the Tractor

Also, keep steps and platforms in good repair and uncluttered. Machine surfaces are intended for your feet and should be kept clear for your feet. That means no pop cans, tow chains, toolboxes, or lunch pails.

Wet grass, mud, or grease may build up on machine surfaces, making it easier to slip while you are on the machine. A slip here could easily bump a control, causing the machine to lurch into action, injuring you or others. That's another reason to keep all machine surfaces clean and uncluttered.

Never jump onto or off of machines. And never attempt to get on or off a machine when it is moving. That's asking for a more-severe injury than an ordinary slip or a fall.

Avoiding Slips and Falls
 • Keep equipment steps and platform clean and free
   of clutter.

 • Act deliberately, never jump off equipment.

 • Wear heavy-duty shoes with non-skid soles.

 • When working in slippery conditions, pay close
   attention to your footing.

STORED ENERGY

Stored energy is energy confined and just waiting to be released. It is completely safe as long as it is confined. But if it is released unexpectedly, stored energy can cause serious injuries.

A simple slingshot shows the concept. You use your energy to stretch the rubber bands. That energy is "stored" in the rubber bands. It is harmless as long as you hold back the rubber bands. But, when you release the slingshot, you release all the energy you used to stretch the rubber bands. The rock comes out of the slingshot with much more force than if you had just thrown the rock.

**ENERGY IS USED TO
STRETCH THE RUBBER BANDS**

**THE ENERGY IS "STORED"
IN THE RUBBER BANDS
UNTIL THE BANDS ARE RELEASED**

Fig. 14 – A Slingshot Demonstrates the Concept of Stored Energy

Here are some systems and components that store energy on outdoor power equipment:

 • **springs**

 • **compressed air**

 • **hydraulic systems.**

Let's look at the hazards presented by each.

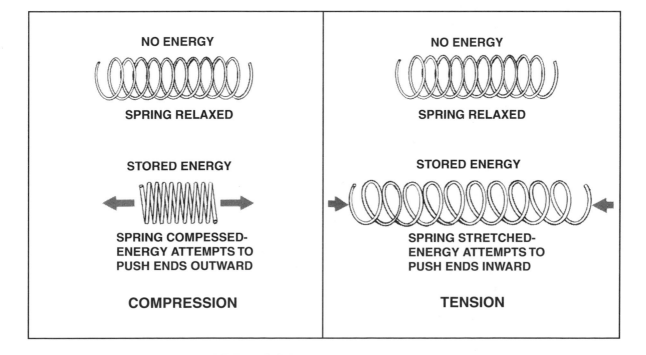

Fig. 15 – Springs can Store Energy in either Compression or Tension

SPRINGS

Springs are energy storing devices. They are used to help lift implements, to keep belts tight, and to absorb shock. Springs store energy in tension or in compression. It is not always obvious which way a spring will move if pressure is released.

To avoid spring-related mishaps, study the situation so you know what will happen before you remove any device connected to a spring. Know what direction the spring will move if it is relaxed. Also note what direction other components will move when the spring is disconnected. Think again of the slingshot. If you release the stored energy slowly, there is no danger of injury. But if the stored energy is released all at once and you are in front of the slingshot, you will very likely get hurt.

COMPRESSED AIR

Compressed air is another form of stored energy, and it can be very dangerous if not properly respected and controlled. When air is compressed, its volume is reduced and energy is stored - the air attempts to return to its original volume. The energy stored by compressed air can be tremendous. For example, a large tractor tire over-inflated to 75 psi (500 kPa) (5 bar) has enough stored energy to lift a 260-pound (120 kg) person a quarter mile (0.4 kilometer) into the air!

When working with compressed air in any situation, remember that stored energy can be very dangerous if it is not properly controlled. Always follow the recommendations of tire and wheel manufacturers, and never over-inflate a tire. It is always a good idea to wear safety glasses when working with compressed air.

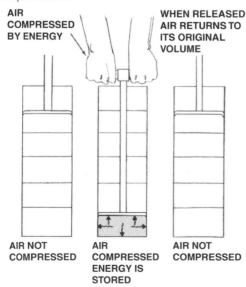

Fig. 16 – When Air is Compressed, Energy is Stored

HYDRAULIC SYSTEMS

Hydraulic systems also store energy. Hydraulic systems must confine fluid under high pressure, often higher than 2,500 pounds per square inch (17,200 kPa) (172 bar).

A lot of energy may be stored in a hydraulic system and because there is often no visible motion, operators do not recognize it as a potential hazard. Carelessly servicing, adjusting, or replacing parts can result in serious injury. Imagine removing a faucet from your kitchen sink without relieving the water pressure. You'd get a face full of water!

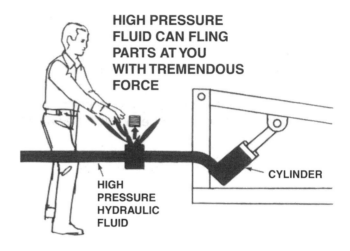

Fig. 17 – Releasing Hydraulic Pressure can Cause Loose Components to Fly Off or a Machine Component to Fall

It is much more dangerous with hydraulic systems. Instead of just getting wet from water at 40 psi (275 kPa) (2.75 bar), you could be seriously injured by oil under 2,500 psi (17,200 kPa) (172 bar) of pressure. Furthermore, releasing hydraulic pressure could cause a loosened component to fly off like a bullet, or an attachment to suddenly fall.

Hydraulic oil can be trapped in the hydraulic system even when the engine is stopped. Trapped oil can be under tremendous pressure. If you loosen a fitting, escaping fluid and moving machine parts could seriously injure you.

Heat can cause another hydraulic hazard. Heat from the sun can expand the hydraulic oil and increase pressure. The pressure can blow seals and move parts of an implement or machine.

A DISCONNECTED IMPLEMENT IN THE RAISED POSITION HAS TRAPPED HYDRAULIC OIL THAT CAN BE UNDER TREMENDOUS PRESSURE.

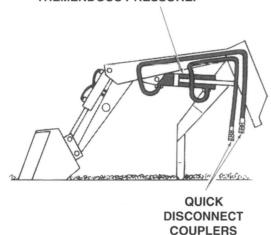

QUICK
DISCONNECT
COUPLERS

Fig. 18 – Even in Disconnected Attachments, Hydraulic Fluid may be Under High Pressure

Avoiding Hydraulic-System Mishaps

Fluid under pressure is just waiting to escape. The same pressures that lets hydraulics do useful work also makes it a force that can be dangerous.

To avoid this hazard, always fully lower attachments or implements and relieve pressure in the hydraulic system before loosening, removing, or adjusting fittings and components.

Follow this procedure even if tightening a hydraulic fitting or component. If you should happen to over-tighten a coupling, it may crack and release a high-pressure stream of hydraulic fluid. The fluid could injure you, plus the attachment may move or drop to the ground.

Before attempting any service:

- **Shut off the engine, which powers the hydraulic pump.**

- **Lower implement or attachment to the ground or onto a solid support.**

- **Move the hydraulic control lever back and forth several times to relieve pressure.**

- **Follow instructions in the operator's manual. Specific procedures for servicing hydraulic systems are very important for your safety.**

OTHER HYDRAULIC CONCERNS

Because hydraulic fluid is under such high pressure, you need to take other special precautions when working with or around **hydraulic systems**.

Pinhole Leaks

If hydraulic fluid under high pressure escapes through an extremely small opening, it comes out as a fine stream. The stream is called a pinhole leak. These leaks can be so small they are hard to see, yet they can be very dangerous. They penetrate skin and flesh, actually injecting hydraulic fluid into the body.

Fig. 19 – The Jet Stream or Mist from a Pinhole Leak can Penetrate Flesh – Do Not Touch

A doctor familiar with this type of injury must surgically remove any fluid injected into the skin within a few hours. If the fluid isn't removed immediately, gangrene may result. Gangrene often leads to amputation. If you ever have oil injected into your skin, get to a doctor immediately, and make sure the doctor understands how to treat the injury.

NEVER feel for hydraulic leaks with bare or even gloved hands.

If your machine has a pinhole leak, it may appear only as dripping fluid. This dripping is actually the result of an invisible high-pressure stream of hydraulic fluid.

Again, never touch a wet hose or machine part with bare or even gloved hands to find the source of the drip. A pinhole leak may be the cause. To locate the leak, wear safety glasses, a heavy protective glove, and then pass a piece of cardboard or wood over the suspected area. Relieve the pressure before correcting the leak.

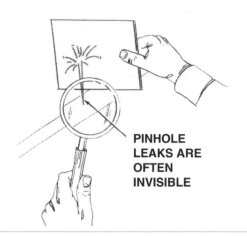

PINHOLE LEAKS ARE OFTEN INVISIBLE

Fig. 20 – Use a Piece of Cardboard or Wood to Find the Leak

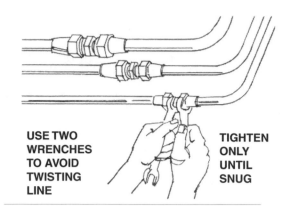

USE TWO WRENCHES TO AVOID TWISTING LINE

TIGHTEN ONLY UNTIL SNUG

Fig. 21 – Use Two Wrenches when Tightening Fittings

Incorrect Coupling

Hooking up a hydraulic line to the wrong tractor outlet can create a hazard. When lines are coupled to the proper port, you get the results you expect. But if lines are crossed, the implement may raise when you expect it to drop. Serious injury could result.

Make sure hydraulic lines are coupled exactly as specified in the operator's manual. Color-code the lines with paint or tape. After you attach the hydraulic lines, try the controls cautiously to see if you get the proper result.

Proper Service

If you replace hydraulic fittings, tubing, or hoses, be sure the new parts meet the pressure requirements of the system. Inadequate parts could fail and cause machine breakdown and personal injury. Use two wrenches when tightening fitting to avoid twisting the lines (Fig. 21).

Outside diameter is not a good indicator of strength or pressure rating. Steel tubing is not necessarily stronger than flexible hoses. Check with your equipment dealer to select proper replacement parts.

Never reassemble fittings that are dirty, chipped, or distorted. Fittings need to be clean and in perfect condition. Keep O-rings and other seals in place. They too should be in perfect condition. Hydraulic systems work under very high pressures. Using materials or components that are not in perfect condition could cause a serious injury.

Matching Pressures

Remember that different tractors generate different hydraulic pressures. Attaching a 2,500 psi (17,200 kPa) (172 bar) system to an implement equipped with hoses, cylinders, and fittings designed for 1,000 psi (6,900 kPa) (69 bar) is inviting trouble. The low-pressure system could burst or explode. Never improvise or adapt fittings or hoses so a high-pressure system can be connected to a low-pressure system.

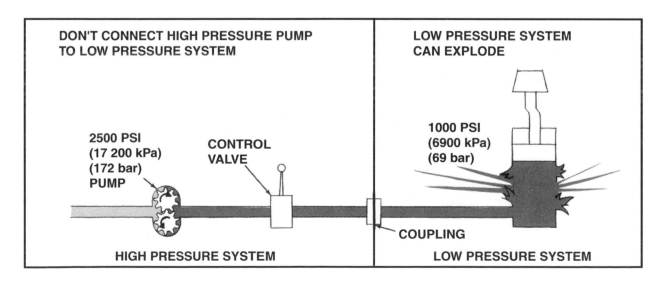

DON'T CONNECT HIGH PRESSURE PUMP TO LOW PRESSURE SYSTEM

LOW PRESSURE SYSTEM CAN EXPLODE

2500 PSI (17 200 kPa) (172 bar) PUMP

CONTROL VALVE

1000 PSI (6900 kPa) (69 bar)

COUPLING

HIGH PRESSURE SYSTEM

LOW PRESSURE SYSTEM

Fig. 22 – Never Connect a High-pressure Hydraulic System to a Low-pressure Implement

DIRECT CURRENT

Battery power is another form of stored energy. But even gasoline engines without batteries have electrical systems that can cause serious injuries. That's because high voltage is required so current can jump the gap on a spark plug. That jumping spark is what causes ignition on gasoline engines.

The voltage on some ignition systems may exceed 25,000 volts. If this high voltage passes through your heart, it could kill you.

That's why you never want to touch spark plug terminals, spark plug cables, or the coil-to-distributor cable while the engine is running. The cable's insulation should protect you— but if it's defective, you'll get a painful shock.

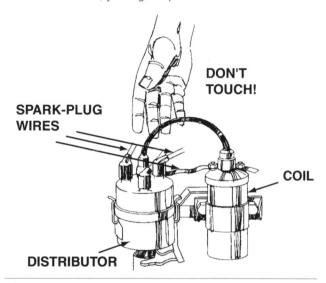

DON'T TOUCH!

SPARK-PLUG WIRES

COIL

DISTRIBUTOR

Fig. 24 – Never Touch Wires when the Ignition Switch is Turned On

Engine electrical systems that are not properly maintained can also cause fires. If bare wire touches a metal part and sparks or becomes hot it can start a fire in dust, chaff, and leaves. Most machinery fires do not result in personal injury, but every fire is a potential source of injury. Inspect electrical systems. Make sure wires are properly insulated, and clean off dust, chaff, leaves, and oil from wires.

TEST YOURSELF

QUESTIONS - CHAPTER 3

1. What are pinch points? Why are they dangerous?

2. Name three types of stored energy.

3. Why do parts freewheel after the engine is shut off?

4. Where should a helper stand when hooking up a 3-point-hitch attachment?

ORGANIZING A SAFETY PROGRAM

INTRODUCTION

Few would disagree with the idea that working safely is good for a business and its employees. After all, who is in favor of working dangerously and work place injuries?

But the reality of making the work place safer and properly training employees is easier said than done. Change is constant—employees change, machines change, jobs change. To keep a company's employees and environment safe, safety efforts have to be ongoing, reacting to the changes in the work force and the work place.

But it's easy for these safety efforts, as important as they are, to fall by the wayside. Often golf courses and landscape businesses are so busy during the summer months, there is hardly time to think, much less keep up with safety issues.

Fig. 1 – During Busy Times Safety Training may be Most Important.

It's during the busy times that safety training may be the most important (Fig. 1). That's why it's important for a business to have an organized safety program. With a safety program in place there are procedures for keeping the work place safe and keeping employees well trained. Safety then becomes a routine part of the business, rather than some extra effort, or something that is saved for rainy days.

THE BENEFITS

An organized safety program offers three important benefits:

- **Protecting employees**
- **Saving money**
- **Preventing or limiting fines.**

Protecting employees may be the most obvious benefit. Properly trained employees will know the correct ways to operate and work around equipment. They will understand what protective clothing and equipment to wear. And they will know how to recognize, and then avoid or correct dangerous situations.

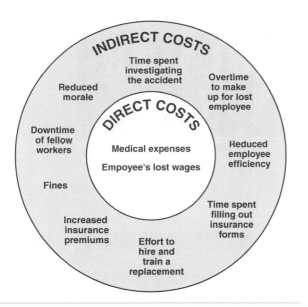

Fig. 2 – Often the Indirect Costs of an Injury are far Greater than the Direct or Out-of-pocket Costs.

Does this effort save money? Indeed it does. Safer employees and a safer work place will limit lost-time mishaps and save money on worker-compensation insurance. As was outlined in Chapter 1, work place injuries are very expensive in both their direct and indirect costs.

IT'S THE LAW

A safety program is also important because it helps employers obey the law. All landscapers, ground-care businesses, and golf courses with one or more employees must abide by the rules and regulations of the Occupational Safety and Health Administration (OSHA). This arm of the United States government is charged with assuring employers provide safe and healthful working conditions.

While the law doesn't tell you what kind of organized safety program you must have, the law does require you do certain things, such as:

- **Minimize hazards**

- **Warn employees of potential hazards**

- **Provide safe tools and equipment**

- **Teach the proper use of personal protective equipment.**

An organized safety program will help you comply with these rules. Plus, if an OSHA inspector visits you it may help you avoid or limit fines. If your safety program shows a good faith effort to follow rules and protect employees, fines for violations are sometimes waived or reduced.

HOW TO GET STARTED

One reason the law doesn't say what kind of safety program a business needs is because every business is different. And while safety programs for similar businesses may be similar, each business will have unique needs it should address.

But businesses are not left totally on their own. OSHA is much more than a safety police officer trying to catch violators. It also works with businesses to help bring safe practices and processes into the work place. That's why OSHA has outlined a four-point plan to help businesses develop their own safety programs.

Here's the plan:

- **Management leadership and employee involvement**

- **Work place analysis**

- **Hazard prevention and control**

- **Safety and health training.**

By following this four-step process, businesses can be well on the road to developing a safety plan that's right for their employees. Let's look at each step of OSHA's recommended plan.

MANAGEMENT LEADERSHIP AND EMPLOYEE INVOLVEMENT

The first step in any successful safety program is for company management to take the lead. If the management of an organization doesn't think safety is important, chances are the employees won't either.

A good first step in showing this safety leadership is to develop a safety policy statement. This statement should be brief—one or two paragraphs—and lay out the importance of complying with all safety rules and regulations. Here's an example of a safety policy statement:

The personal safety and health of each employee is of primary importance to this business. No employee is expected to use equipment or perform a job until he or she has received proper instructions. No employee is required to work at a job he or she knows is not safe. All employees are expected to help detect and control hazards that can produce injuries. Inform your supervisor immediately of any unsafe situations beyond your ability or authority to control.

There is not an exact format for a company's safety policy statement. What's important is that it expresses the business's concern for safety and lays out some general goals and responsibilities for employees.

JOB SAFETY & HEALTH PROTECTION

The Occupational Safety and Health Act of 1970 provides job safety and health protection for workers by promoting safe and healthful working conditions throughout the Nation. Provisions of the Act include the following:

Employers

All employers must furnish to employees employment and a place of employment free from recognized hazards that are causing or are likely to cause death or serious harm to employees. Employers must comply with occupational safety and health standards issued under the Act.

Employees

Employees must comply with all occupational safety and health standards, rules, regulations and orders issued under the Act that apply to their own actions and conduct on the job.

The Occupational Safety and Health Administration (OSHA) of the U.S. Department of Labor has the primary responsibility for administering the Act. OSHA issues occupational safety and health standards, and its Compliance Safety and Health Officers conduct jobsite inspections to help ensure compliance with the Act

Inspection

The Act requires that a representative of the employer and a representative authorized by the employees be given an opportunity to accompany the OSHA inspector for the purpose of aiding the inspection.

Where there is no authorized employee representative, the OSHA Compliance Officer must consult with a reasonable number of employees concerning safety and health conditions in the workplace.

Complaint

Employees or their representatives have the right to file a complaint with the nearest OSHA office requesting an inspection if they believe unsafe or unhealthful conditions exist in their workplace. OSHA will withhold, on request, names of employees complaining.

The Act provides that employees may not be discharged or discriminated against in any way for filing safety and health complaints or for otherwise exercising their rights under the Act.

Employees who believe they have been discriminated against may file a complaint with their nearest OSHA office within 30 days of the alleged discriminatory action.

Citation

If upon inspection OSHA believes an employer has violated the Act, a citation alleging such violations will be issued to the employer. Each citation will specify a time period within which the alleged violation must be corrected

The OSHA citation must be prominently displayed at or near the place of alleged violation for three days, or until it is corrected, whichever is later, to warn employees of dangers that may exist there.

Proposed Penalty

The Act provides for mandatory civil penalties against employers of up to $7,000 for each serious violation and for optional penalties of up to $7,000 for each nonserious violation. Penalties of up to $7,000 per day may be proposed for failure to correct violations within the proposed time period and for each day the violation continues beyond the prescribed abatement date. Also, any employer who willfully or repeatedly violates the Act may be assessed penalties of up to $70,000 for each such violation. A minimum penalty of $5,000 may be imposed for each willful violation. A violation of posting requirements can bring a penalty of up to $7,000.

There are also provisions for criminal penalties. Any willful violation resulting in the death of any employee, upon conviction, is punishable by a fine of up to $250,000 (or $500,000 if the employer is a corporation), or by imprisonment for up to six months, or both. A second conviction of an employer doubles the possible term of imprisonment. Falsifying records, reports, or applications is punishable by a fine of $10,000 or up to six months in jail or both.

Voluntary Activity

While providing penalties for violations, the Act also encourages efforts by labor and management, before an OSHA inspection, to reduce workplace hazards voluntarily and to develop and improve safety and health programs in all workplaces and industries. OSHA's Voluntary Protection Programs recognize outstanding efforts of this nature.

OSHA has published Safety and Health Program Management Guidelines to assist employers in establishing or perfecting programs to prevent or control employee exposure to workplace hazards. There are many public and private organizations that can provide information and assistance in this effort, if requested. Also, your local OSHA office can provide considerable help and advice on solving safety and health problems or can refer you to other sources for help such as training.

Consultation

Free assistance in identifying and correcting hazards and in improving safety and health management is available to employers, without citation or penalty, through OSHA-supported programs in each State. These programs are usually administered by the State Labor or Health department or a State university.

Posting Instructions

Employers in States operating OSHA approved State Plans should obtain and post the State's equivalent poster.

Under provisions of Title 29, Code of Federal Regulations, Part 1903 2(a)(1) employers must post this notice (or facsimile) in a conspicuous place where notices to employees are customarily posted.

More Information

Additional information and copies of the Act, OSHA safety and health standards, and other applicable regulations may be obtained from your employer or from the nearest OSHA Regional Office in the following locations:

Atlanta, GA	(404) 562-2300
Boston, MA	(617) 565-9860
Chicago, IL	(312) 353-2220
Dallas, TX	(214) 767-4731
Denver, CO	(303) 844-1600
Kansas City, MO	(816) 426-5861
New York, NY	(212) 337-2378
Philadelphia, PA	(215) 596-1201
San Francisco, CA	(415) 975-4310
Seattle, WA	(206) 553-5930

Washington, DC
1997 (Reprinted)
OSHA 2203

Alexis M. Herman, Secretary of Labor

U.S. Department of Labor
Occupational Safety and Health Administration

This information will be made available to sensory impaired individuals upon request.
Voice phone: (202) 219-8615; TDD message referral phone: 1-800-326-2577.

GPO : 1997 o - 429-604 QL 3

Fig. 3 – Job Safety & Health Protection Bulletin

Once a business has a new or revised safety policy statement, it's important to share that safety statement with the employees. This is an important first step in gaining "employee involvement." Many businesses also post their policy statement next to the "Job Safety & Health Protection" poster (#OSHA 2203) that each employer is required to display in a prominent place (Fig 3).

Besides posting the policy statement, it's a good idea to hold a meeting with all employees to discuss the policy and business objectives for safety and health. This should be done annually and with each new employee before he or she starts the job. To have true employee involvement, workers must understand company policy and feel free to discuss their concerns and ideas with management.

WHO'S IN CHARGE

Another crucial step in getting a safety program rolling is to assign responsibility for safety efforts. Generally this means appointing a safety coordinator.

This safety coordinator will be responsible for coming up with specific plans, and turning those plans into actions. Experience has shown if there isn't a coordinator, it is all too easy for safety issues to be put off for a more convenient time. With a coordinator keeping on top of safety issues, it is much more likely the safety program will become a routine, ongoing effort.

Of course it's important that business owners or senior management continue to have some involvement in the program and set a good safety example by abiding by all safety rules. For example, if safety glasses are required in certain areas, all workers, from top to bottom, need to wear them at all times. Nothing undermines an employee's commitment to safety efforts like seeing management ignore company safety rules.

Once management and employees have started down the road to greater safety involvement, a business can build on that involvement with the next step in the process: work site analysis.

WORK SITE ANALYSIS

It is a business's responsibility under the law to provide a safe work place. But how does someone know a work place is unsafe? The answer is by a work site analysis. It is a process that helps businesses identify areas, situations, or processes that by their nature may make a work place injury more likely.

Fig. 4 – A Work Site Analysis Looks for Potential Hazards

Basically this involves checking out the work place and equipment for potential hazards. This may sound like a large task, but it doesn't have to be. Many hazards are easy to find, and fix, once you start looking.

For example:

- **Replacing damaged safety glasses**
- **Cleaning up litter and debris**
- **Adding or replacing fire extinguishers**
- **Repairing damaged or missing shields**
- **Clearing steps of debris**
- **Restocking or replacing first aid kits.**

Once a hazard is found, make an action plan. The written plan should include: the hazard, corrective measures, target completion date, and who is responsible.

GET SOME HELP

There are many resources available to help with a work site analysis. The first resource should be the business's employees. They can tell you where they have had injuries or near misses. They may also know of things like loose railings, sharp metal edges, or missing shields that pose hazards.

Your state can help. Each state has a free **Consultation Program** that is largely funded by OSHA. With this service, a safety consultant will come to a business and inspect its facilities and processes. The consultant will then list potential safety and health problems and recommend solutions. The program is confidential and totally separate from OSHA's inspection division. No citations or fines are given as a result of this voluntary inspection.

A business's insurance carrier may be of assistance. An insurance company has a vested interest in limiting injuries. They may offer safety checklists that will suggest common trouble spots.

Expert private consultants are also available. Check the Yellow Pages under "Safety Consultants."

There are also OSHA publications and checklists available to help you do your own work site analysis. See "Additional Resources" at the end of this chapter.

FOLLOW-UP INSPECTIONS

Once a business has done an initial work site analysis, regular follow-up inspections are needed to make sure no new hazards have appeared. This is usually done by routine self-inspections. Check lists work well for this task. A business may appoint a team of employees to carefully look at each job and look for hidden hazards in the equipment or procedures.

But businesses should not rely on only these inspections to identify problems. Each business should have some simple procedure for employees to inform supervisors about things that look harmful. Employees should also feel empowered and responsible to report or correct any potentially dangerous situations they find.

HAZARD PREVENTION AND CONTROL

Once a business knows its hazards and potential hazards, it is ready to put in place systems to prevent or control those hazards.

As mentioned in the previous section, some hazards will be easy to eliminate. Simple repairs or better housekeeping will take care of some problems. A simple action plan, like Fig. 5 created by OSHA, can help keep track of hazards found during the work site analysis. The sheets also document what corrective measures have been taken.

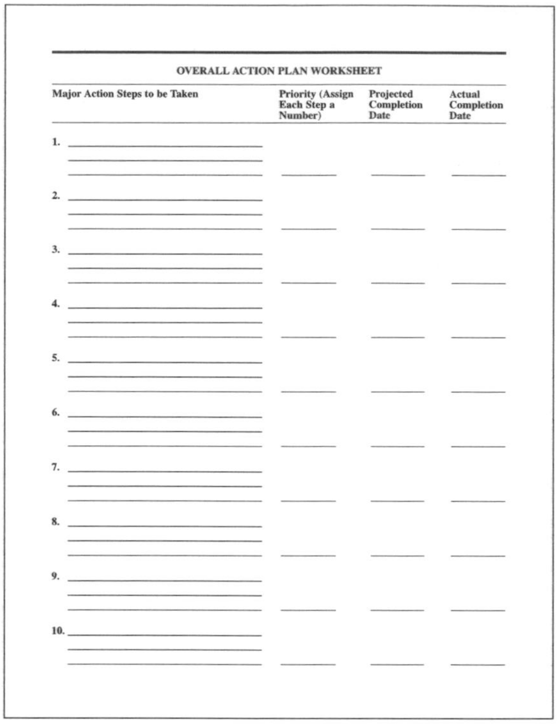
OVERALL ACTION PLAN WORKSHEET

Major Action Steps to be Taken	Priority (Assign Each Step a Number)	Projected Completion Date	Actual Completion Date
1.			
2.			
3.			
4.			
5.			
6.			
7.			
8.			
9.			
10.			

Fig. 5 – Make an Action Plan to Track Hazards and their Control

Controlling some other hazards may take changing procedures. There may need to be a better way for employees to report a damaged or missing shield. Since well-maintained machines run better and are safer to operate, there may need to be an improved system to assure routine maintenance is done on time. New company policies or rules may be needed—"No smoking while refueling" or "Work boots and long pants must be worn when using power equipment." Having employees involved in developing these new policies will improve their understanding and acceptance of rule changes.

Some hazard controls may take more technical advice. If the business uses a highly toxic chemical, perhaps a less-toxic chemical can be found that will do the same job. If not, perhaps better personal protective equipment (PPE) may control the hazard presented by the highly toxic chemical.

For this kind of technical help a business can contact its state safety consultation program, chemical sales representative, university extension office, or trade association.

INVESTIGATING MISHAPS

Another source of hazard-control information can come from investigating mishaps and injuries. Just as the government investigates all airplane crashes to find the cause, so too a company should investigate all of its injuries. These investigations will help discover why the incident happened. Could it have been prevented by better housekeeping, or by the use of proper PPE, or by a better procedure? The answers to these questions may point to some processes or hazardous situations that need attention.

Fig. 6 – Investigating an Incident will Help Find the Cause

What caused the fall in Fig. 6? Was it a broken step, improper shoes, a slippery tractor platform, or a careless employee? Investigating an incident will help find the cause.

To make the investigation process easier and more thorough, you can use standard injury-investigation forms. These forms are available from insurance companies and safety organizations.

Once a business has put hazard prevention and control efforts in place, it's important to do follow-up evaluations. Be sure the efforts really are controlling the hazards, and that all employees are following new rules and procedures.

This Could Be You ...I'll never forget it. It was my first day of working at the golf course. I was helping John cut down a dead tree. John was actually cutting, I was to stay out of the way, and once the tree was down, help load up the branches. I don't know exactly what happened, but I heard a loud crack, and I looked up and saw this huge limb break off the tree and fall on top of John. His leg was broken and I could see the bone, plus he was bleeding badly. We had no first-aid kit and I knew I needed to get help. But I had no idea where I was, other than somewhere on the back nine.

MEDICAL AND FIRE EMERGENCIES

Another part of a business's hazard prevention and control program should concern emergency response—namely medical and fire emergencies.

For medical emergencies, here is what OSHA recommends:

- Have in place an emergency medical procedure for handling injuries, transporting ill or injured workers, and notifying medical facilities. This will limit confusion if an emergency happens.
- Have procedures for reporting employee injuries or illness that are simple and easily understood by all employees.
- Be sure adequate first-aid supplies are readily available. Businesses are required to have someone trained and readily available to render first aid. Contact the local Red Cross, or a safety supplier for advice on first-aid training and appropriate first-aid kits for your business.
- Be sure battery-charging stations and any other areas with corrosive materials have the required eyewash facilities and showers.
- Consider retaining a local doctor or an occupational health nurse on a part-time or as-needed basis to advise the business on medical and first aid issues.

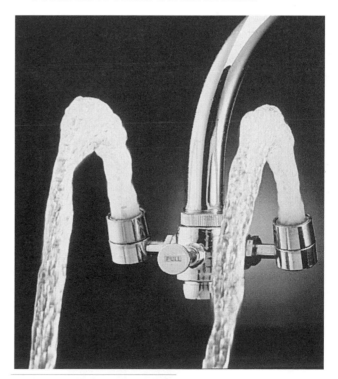

Fig. 7 – Emergency Eyewash Facility
(Photo Courtesy of Gempler's Inc.)

Battery charging stations and other areas with corrosive materials need to have emergency eyewash facilities (Fig. 7).

GETTING HELP WHERE IT'S NEEDED

To assure the prompt response of fire and other emergency personnel, an emergency information sheet should be posted by all work site phones, kept with cellular phones, and mounted in trucks and trailers that take equipment off site. This sheet should include phone numbers for:

- **Fire department**
- **Sheriff/police**
- **Ambulance**
- **Doctor**
- **Poison control center**
- **Electric/gas company**
- **Chemtrec 800-424-9300, for chemical spills.**

This emergency information sheet should also include directions to your place of business. For mobile work crews, there should also be addresses of clients or work sites. A first-aid kit and instructions should be handy in case of an injury. Each off-site crew should have one.

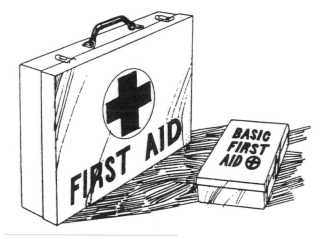

Fig. 8 – First-Aid Kit and Instructions

If workers are at a large site, such as an office complex, park, or golf course, a map of the location may be needed to help direct emergency personnel to an injury site.

FIRE!

The best protection against fire is a good prevention program. That should be part of any hazard-control program. But if a fire starts, company employees should be ready to take immediate action. That's why all employees should understand what to do in case of a fire.

The first step is to sound a fire alarm so other employees can evacuate or offer assistance. As part of employee training, everyone should know how to sound the alarm. This may be as simple as yelling "FIRE!" in a very small organization.

Larger companies may have a fire-alarm system. Employees must know how to sound this alarm, and if the alarm automatically calls the fire department.

If the alarm does not call the fire department automatically, someone should immediately make the call. Even if the employee thinks someone might be able to extinguish the fire on his own, the fire department should be called. Fire fighters would rather show up at a fire that has already been extinguished than fight a fire that has gone out of control because employees waited to make the call.

Once the fire department has been contacted, employees can try to fight the fire if it can be done safely. Here is another example where proper safety training can prevent a huge business loss.

FIRE EXTINGUISHERS

To understand fire extinguishers, you first need to understand about the different types of fires. The three most common types of fires are (Fig. 9):

- **Class A—Combustibles like paper and wood**
- **Class B—Gasoline, diesel fuel, grease, and solvents**
- **Class C—Electrical-equipment fires**

(Class D fires involve combustible metals and are generally not a concern to landscape firms or golf courses.)

Class A fires, burning paper, wood, cloth, rubbish, etc can be controlled by water, so a water hose may do the trick.

However putting water on a Class B or Class C fire could have dire consequences. Water tends to spread Class B fires— burning petroleum products or solvents. With Class C (electrical) fires, water may conduct electricity, giving you a severe shock. For Class B and C fires you must use an appropriate fire extinguisher or some other way to smother the fire. Understanding the three main types of fires will help you fight them safely.

CLASS A FIRES	PAPER, WOOD, CLOTH EXCELSIOR, RUBBISH ETC. WHERE QUENCHING AND COOLING EFFECT OF WATER IS NEEDED
CLASS B FIRES	BURNING LIQUIDS (GASO-LINE, OILS, PAINT, ETC. WHERE SMOTHERING EFFECT IS REQUIRED
CLASS C FIRES	FIRES IN LIVE ELECTRICAL EQUIPMENT (MOTORS SWITCHES, HEATERS, ETC.) WHERE A NON-CONDUCT-ING EXTINGUISHING AGENT IS REQUIRED

Fig. 9 – Three Main Types of Fires

Fire extinguishers use these same fire classification letters to show the kinds of fires they can put out. Ones labeled A:B:C are capable of handling all three types of common fires.

Fire extinguishers also use a number in front of the letters to indicate the size of fire, for that category, that the extinguisher can put out. (No size is assigned to electrical, or "C" fires.) For example, an extinguisher rated 10-B, can put out a grease fire twice as large as an extinguisher labeled 5-B.

While a fire extinguisher rated for all classes of fire—A, B, and C—is versatile, you may want to select one best suited for its location. For example, an extinguisher with a high B rating might be best for a petroleum storage area. Contact the local fire department for advice on selecting and then installing the right fire extinguisher for each work-place situation.

If a business has crews that work off site, a fire extinguisher should be part of the equipment that travels to each job site.

SAFETY AND HEALTH TRAINING

The last step in building an effective safety program is proper training. Safety training will help everyone in the work place do their jobs properly. Plus it will help every employee understand what hazards are involved in their jobs and how these hazards are controlled.

Safety training can take many forms. Often it can be included in training the business already does.

For example, when a worker is trained on a new machine, make sure he or she understands the potential hazards and reviews safe operating procedures. Point out the warning signs on the equipment. Have the worker read the operator's manual, paying special attention to safety concerns. And be sure the worker understands the work clothes and personal protective equipment that is needed.

Fig. 10 – Have Regularly Scheduled Safety Meetings

Regularly scheduled safety meetings will help employees understand how to prevent and control work-site hazards.

Other safety training may take a more formal, classroom-type approach. Many organizations find a monthly safety meeting works well. These meetings should be mandatory for all employees, and take place on company time. Early morning meetings, with coffee, donuts, and fruit work best for many organizations. After work, employees may be too tired to give the information full attention. What's important is not exactly what the training looks like, but rather that the employees understand work-place hazards and how to control them.

Pay special attention to new employees as well as current employees moving to new jobs. They have new safety skills to learn. Supervisors need to know all the hazards their staff's face, and be ready to reinforce training with quick safety reminders. They may need to use discipline to reinforce the importance of following safety procedures.

TRAINING HELP

There are many resources available to help with safety training:

- **The National Safety Council (800-621-7619) offers a wide range of safety handouts and other training aids.**
- **Cooperative Extension Service**
- **A business insurance agent**
- **Professional association**
- **Outdoor-power-equipment dealer**
- **Local fire department**
- **Red Cross**
- **Safety supply store**
- **Mail order supply company such as Gempler's, 1-800-332-6744**
- **State Consultation program (check out "consultation services" on the OSHA website: www.osha.gov).**

And don't forget to ask your competitors for their training ideas. They face similar challenges and may have found good safety training materials.

All this training may seem like a burden, but it's too important to ignore. Only when workers understand what hazards are present in the work place, and understand what to do about those hazards, can they perform their jobs safely. Doing anything less is leaving safety to chance, and against the law.

HAZARD COMMUNICATION STANDARD

If a business's employees work with, or around, hazardous chemicals, there is one more important component to a safety program. It concerns the **Hazard Communication Standard**.

The Hazard Communication Standard (HCS) is an OSHA regulation that requires employers to inform workers of any chemical hazards on the job and to train workers how to protect themselves from the hazards. These regulations are sometimes called "Worker Right to Know." The basic goal of the HCS is to assure employers and employees know about chemical–related work hazards and how to protect themselves.

This Could Be You...Ivan just could not shake the flu. He'd had the chills and headaches for over three weeks. He'd never been sick like this. Then he realized he got the "flu" about the same time he started a new job in the greenhouse. Maybe it wasn't the flu after all. Ivan talked to his supervisor and they checked out the material safety data sheets for all the chemicals being used in the greenhouse. This led them to check out the personal protective equipment. On close inspection they found a crack in the respirator Ivan had been using. Two weeks later, after a medical checkup and a new respirator, Ivan was feeling much better.

To comply with the law, businesses must have a written hazard communication program in place. There are six main steps to complying with the standard:

- **Name someone responsible for the tasks**
- **Compile a list of all chemicals used in the business**
- **Make sure that all chemical containers are properly labeled**
- **File a Material Safety Data Sheet (MSDS) for each chemical**
- **Train workers on how to find and read labels and MSDSs**
- **Train workers on use and maintenance of personal protective equipment.**

Once someone has been appointed to lead the hazard communication efforts, the first job is making a list of all chemicals the business uses. Past purchase records may be helpful, as will an inventory of the work place. Chemicals are more than just liquids in containers. For the purposes of the hazard communication standard, chemicals include liquids, solids, mists, and gasses. Herbicides and pesticides are included, as are fertilizers, gasoline, petroleum products, solvents, and cleaners.

Once the chemical list is prepared, labels are the next concern. The label is important not only because it identifies the chemical, but because it also provides important health and safety information. Labels also tell workers how to limit their exposure to chemicals. Chemical manufacturers and importers are required to have labels on all chemical containers they ship.

Once the chemical is delivered to a business, it should be kept in its original container (except for certain exceptions like portable fuel cans) and the label should be intact. Having all chemicals properly labeled will help protect employee health and safety, and prevent the misuse of a chemical product.

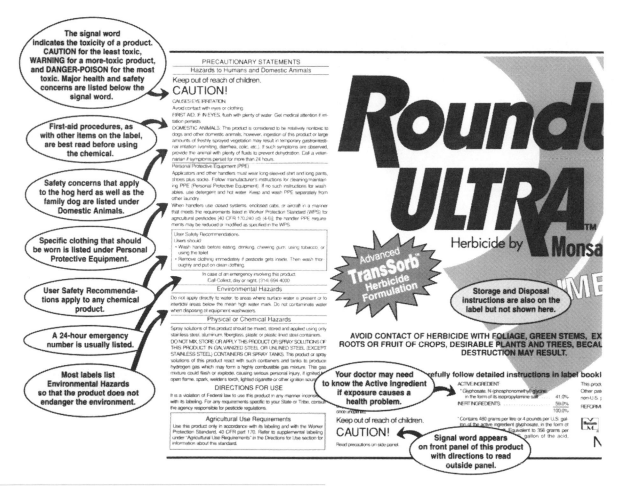

The signal word indicates the toxicity of a product. CAUTION for the least toxic, WARNING for a more-toxic product, and DANGER-POISON for the most toxic. Major health and safety concerns are listed below the signal word.

First-aid procedures, as with other items on the label, are best read before using the chemical.

Safety concerns that apply to the hog herd as well as the family dog are listed under Domestic Animals.

Specific clothing that should be worn is listed under Personal Protective Equipment.

User Safety Recommendations apply to any chemical product.

A 24-hour emergency number is usually listed.

Most labels list Environmental Hazards so that the product does not endanger the environment.

Your doctor may need to know the Active Ingredient if exposure causes a health problem.

Storage and Disposal instructions are also on the label but not shown here.

Signal word appears on front panel of this product with directions to read outside panel.

Fig. 11 – Labels on Chemical Products List Important Safety Information

MATERIAL SAFETY DATA SHEETS

While the label has a certain amount of health and safety information, more in-depth information about a chemical product can be found on a **material safety data sheet** (MSDS).

Chemical manufacturers or importers must prepare an MSDS for each chemical they market. They must also provide the MSDS to people and businesses that buy the chemical. Some of the information found on an MSDS includes:

- **Physical and chemical characteristics**
- **Physical and health hazards**
- **Precautions for safe use**
- **Fire and explosion hazard data**
- **Toxicity**
- **Symptoms from exposure to the chemical**
- **Emergency first-aid procedures**
- **Name and address of manufacturer.**

It is an employer's responsibility to have on file an MSDS for each chemical used in the business. These MSDSs must also be readily available to all employees.

The goal of this part of the hazard communication standard is to make it easy for employees to check out the health and safety information on chemicals they are exposed to.

REQUIRED TRAINING

With the safety and health information of labels and MSDSs in place, the next step of the process is employee training.

OSHA recommends the employee training program include:

- **An explanation of the basics of the hazard communication standard**
- **How to read a label and an MSDS**
- **Where employees can find the firm's MSDSs**
- **Chemicals used in the work place**
- **How employees can protect themselves from these chemicals**
- **How to use recommended PPE.**

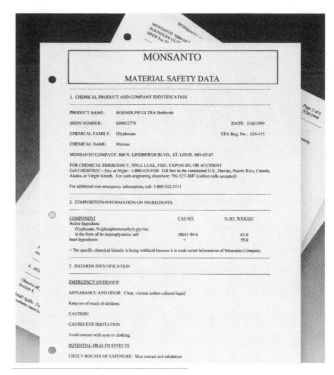

Fig. 12 – Material Safety Data Sheets

A material safety data sheet contains lots of health and safety information (Fig. 12). There should be one on file for each chemical used in a business

This training can easily be incorporated into a firm's regular safety training program. Again, the rules are not concerned with how the training is done, but rather that all employees understand what chemical hazards exist at a business and how they can protect themselves. For more information on compliance with the Hazard Communication Standard, contact your local OSHA office, or see "Additional Resources" at the end of this chapter.

DOCUMENTING SAFETY ACTIVITIES

Records of sales, costs, profits, and losses are essential to all successful businesses. They enable the owner or manager to learn from experience and make corrections for future operations.

Records of safety-related activities serve the same purpose. A good safety record-keeping program will document:

- **Efforts to start and maintain a safety program**

- **A company's safety policy**

- **Safety and health meetings**

- **PPE training activities**

- **A company's written hazardous communication program.**

Keeping track of work-related injuries and illnesses also makes sense, as it helps pinpoint unsafe conditions and/or procedures. (Employers with 11 or more employees are required to maintain records of occupational injuries and illnesses as they occur. Contact the nearest OSHA office for more information and exact rules.)

All these records will help a business see what it has accomplished, and plan for what still needs to get done. Plus the records will show to an OSHA inspector that you are following work-place safety rules and regulations.

ADDITIONAL RESOURCES

Small Business Safety and Health Manual, National Safety Council, Itasca, IL

Keller's Official OSHA Safety Handbook, J.J. Keller Assoc., Neenah, WI; ph. 920-772-2848

OSHA Handbook for Small Business (OSHA #2209)

Hazard Communication Guidelines for Compliance (OSHA # 3111)

Hazard Communication—A Compliance Kit (OSHA #3104)

These and other OSHA booklets are available online at www.osha.gov, or from the Superintendent of Documents, U.S. Government Printing Office, P.O. Box 37194, Pittsburgh, PA, ph. 202-512-1800

Hazard Communication Compliance Kit (#GRTK) serves as a basis for a company's hazard communication program. Gempler's 800-383-8473

Safety and Health Resource Guide for Small Business (#2000-148) lists sources of free occupational health and safety information. Contact the National Institute for Occupational Safety and Health at 800-356-4674 or www.cdc.gov/niosh

Employee Safety, an information packet compiled by the Golf Course Superintendents Association of America, 1412 Research Park Drive, Lawrence, KS; ph. 800-472-7878

Find information on work-site safety and health and download many OSHA booklets, and regulations. www.osha.gov

The Canadian Centre for Occupational Health and Safety has safety information and publications of interest to Canadian businesses. www.canoshweb.org

TEST YOURSELF

QUESTIONS - CHAPTER 4

1. What are three benefits of having a workplace safety program?

2. Name four general things OSHA regulations require a business to do.

3. Why is it important for a business to have a safety coordinator?

4. Why should all workers know where MSDSs are filed?

COMPACT TRACTORS

Fig. 1 – Compact Tractors have between 20 and 40 Horsepower

INTRODUCTION

Just what is a **compact tractor**? While there is no official definition for the term "compact tractor", for the purposes of this book, a compact tractor has between 20 and 40 horsepower.

This size of tractor is most popular with landscapers, grounds keepers, and golf course superintendents. Safety information in this chapter also generally applies to tractors with more than 40 horsepower. Safety information for lawn tractors is covered in Chapter 8.

IS TRACTOR SAFETY IMPORTANT?

Tractor-related mishaps in the United States kill more than 300 people each year. That means someone will probably die today, and tomorrow, and the next day as a result of a tractor-related incident.

This is a startling number, especially since experience shows most of these fatalities could have been prevented.

The majority of these tractor-related mishaps can be divided into six major categories:

1. **Tractor upsets (overturns, rollovers, etc.)**
2. **Runovers (by tractors or implements)**
3. **Falls**
4. **Hitching mishaps**
5. **PTO (power take off) entanglements**
6. **Collisions with motor vehicles**

Lets look at each of these categories and see how these incidents happen and how they can be avoided.

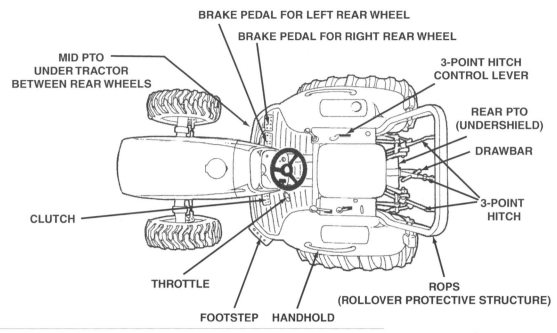

Fig. 2 – A Bird's Eye View of some of the Features Generally found on a Compact Tractor

TRACTOR UPSETS

Tractor upsets; meaning the tractor rolls over sideways or backwards, are the number one cause of tractor fatalities in the United States.

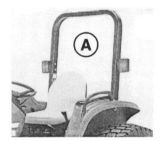

Fig. 3 – Types of ROPS Typically Found on Compact Tractors

But before we discuss how upsets happen and how they can be prevented, it's important to understand that tractor rollovers, and other upsets, don't have to cause serious injuries. There is a simple way to prevent most injuries that result from tractor upsets. It's calls a **ROPS**.

There are three types of ROPS typically found on compact tractors (see Fig. 3).

- **A – 2-post ROPS**
- **B – foldable ROPS that is popular with tractor owners who have low sheds or must work around low growing trees**
- **C – ROPS tractor cab**

ROPS stands for **r**oll**o**ver **p**rotective **s**tructure. It's a frame, sometimes built into a cab that protects the operator in case of a tractor upset. John Deere engineers first designed it in the 1960's.

HOW A ROPS WORKS

In most cases the ROPS limits the upset to 90 degrees, or a one-quarter roll. That means if the tractor upsets, it won't roll all the way upside down. Even if the upset goes beyond 90 degrees, the ROPS can support the weight of the tractor, thus protecting the operator from being crushed.

If a tractor with a ROPS rolls over, the ROPS generally limits the roll to a quarter turn (Fig. 4). It offers great protection, only if the operator wears a seatbelt.

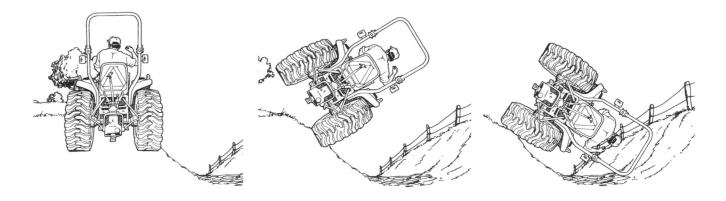

Fig. 4 – Rollovers with Tractors with ROPS will Generally be Limited to a Quarter Turn

ROPS SAVES LIVES

Without a ROPS, there is a 75% chance that the operator will **not** survive a rollover. If the tractor has a ROPS and **the operator wears the seatbelt**, there is a 95% chance of the operator walking away from a tractor upset.

Fig. 6 – Always Wear a Seatbelt when Operating a Tractor with ROPS

If every tractor that had an upset was equipped with a ROPS, and the operator wore his or her seatbelt, nearly 130 lives could be saved each year. In Europe, where ROPS use is required, deaths from rollovers are limited to just two or three per year.

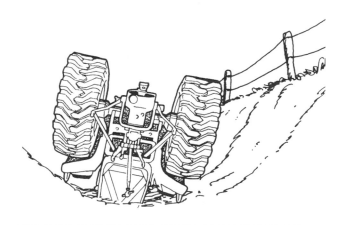

Fig. 5 – Without ROPS, the Operator has a 75% Chance of Being Killed

While all tractors built today come with ROPS, many tractors built before 1985 were sold without ROPS.

You should never work with a tractor that is not equipped with a ROPS and functioning seatbelts. When working with a tractor equipped with ROPS, always wear your seatbelt.

So follow these two important safety rules:

1. **If you operate a tractor with a ROPS, wear your seatbelt at all times.**

2. **If your tractor doesn't have a ROPS, get one installed. Even if the tractor never had a ROPS, there's a good chance one is available, either from the original manufacturer or another supplier.**

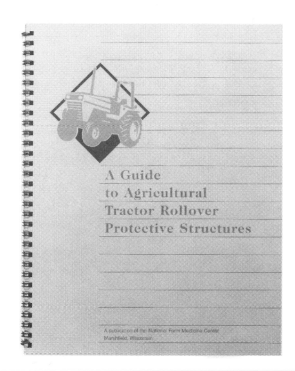

Fig. 7 – A Guide To Agricultural Tractor Rollover Protective Structures

For a list of ROPS manufacturers and the tractors their products will fit, contact the National Farm Medicine Center, 1000 North Oak Avenue, Marshfield, WI 54449-5790, phone 1-800-662-6900. Ask for *A Guide To Agricultural Tractor Rollover Protective Structures*. The guide can also be accessed at *http://www.marshmed.org/nfmc/*.

Besides ROPS, there is another, similar operator protection available, FOPS. It stands for <u>F</u>alling <u>O</u>bject <u>P</u>rotective <u>S</u>tructure. FOPS provide both rollover protection, and as the name implies, operator protection from falling objects.

Fig. 8 – A FOPS has a Sturdy Metal Roof

Protection from falling objects could be important at certain construction sites, during pallet-fork work, or at any job where falling objects pose a potential hazard. Be sure you don't confuse a FOPS, which has a heavy-duty metal roof, with the fiberglass canopies that are intended only to protect the operator from the sun and rain.

Fig. 9 – A Fiberglass Canopy Only Protects the Operator from Sun or Light Rain. It is Not a FOPS.

The fiberglass canopy that is found on some compact tractors only protects the operator from sun or light rain. These canopies are not considered FOPS (Fig. 9).

UPSETS HAPPEN FAST

Some tractor drivers think their quick reactions will save them from a tractor upset. They think if an upset starts to happen, they'll be able to react fast enough to prevent an injury.

The fact of the matter is that tractor upsets can happen very fast. Plus, they generally surprise the operator. Before there is time to react, it is too late.

For example, in a backward tip, the tractor can be all the way upside down in less than 1-1/2 seconds. A rollover to the side can happen in less than one second. There is no time to jump clear because before the driver knows what is happening, the upset has occurred.

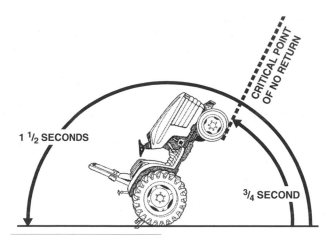

CRITICAL POINT OF NO RETURN

1 ½ SECONDS

¾ SECOND

Fig. 10 – Rollovers Happen Fast

That's why it is so important to understand how tractor upsets happen. If you understand how upsets can happen, you'll be better able to avoid those situations.

CAUSES OF ROLLOVERS TO THE REAR

Anytime there is a tractor upset; one or more of the following four forces generally cause it:

- **Leverage on the drawbar or hitch**
- **Rear-axle torque**
- **Centrifugal force**
- **Gravity**

The first two forces most often result in rollovers to the rear. Let's look at these forces and how to counteract them.

FORCE 1: LEVERAGE ON THE DRAWBAR OR HITCH

When pulling a heavy load, the rear tires push against the ground with considerable force. At the same time, the load attached to the tractor hitch pulls back against the forward movement of the tractor. When this happens, the point of contact between the rear tires and the ground serves as a pivot point. The load attempts to pivot the tractor and raise the front tires off the ground.

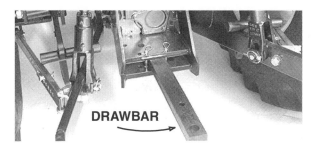

DRAWBAR

Fig. 11 – Tractor Drawbar

The amount of pull (draft) and the height of the hitch point determine the force of the pivoting action. Generally there is not a problem. If the load is attached to the tractor drawbar, and the drawbar is set at the recommended height, and the tractor is properly ballasted, a rollover will not occur. Instead, the rear wheels will slip, or the engine will stall before overturning occurs.

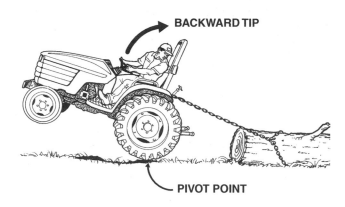

BACKWARD TIP

PIVOT POINT

Fig. 12 – A Load Hitched Above the Normal Drawbar Height

If the load is hitched above the normal drawbar height, the chances of a backward tip are greatly increased (Fig. 12).

The real danger comes when the load is attached too high (thus increasing the leverage of the pull). Even a light load attached too high can quickly tip a tractor backwards.

This Could Be You…The skid steer loader was stuck again and Dave wasn't sure his tractor would have enough traction in this smeary mess to pull it out. Then Dave had a "brilliant" idea. If he attached the tow chain higher on the tractor, it would put more downward pressure on the tires (or so he thought) and that would give him more traction. He hooked one end of the chain to the skid steer and the other end to his tractor, up on a bracket behind the seat. Dave slowly pulled the chain tight, and then fully let out the clutch. In an instant, the tractor reared up tossing Dave backward off the seat and onto the ground. The tractor, now without a driver, was spinning in the mud; its front tires about three feet off the ground. Dave scrambled out of the way – safe. If the mud hadn't limited traction, the tractor surely would have flipped all the way over, crushing him. By hitching the tow chain high, he unknowingly had increased the leverage, and the likelihood of a backward tip.

SAFETY ALERT: Holes are provided on the frames of some tractors for attaching mounted implements and other devices. Do not use these holes to attach a chain, towrope, or other pulling device. Only pull from the drawbar.

FORCE 2: REAR AXLE TORQUE

Engaging the clutch applies torque (twisting force) to the rear axle of the tractor. Normally the axle turns and the tractor moves ahead. But if the axle movement is restrained in some way, say by a very heavy load, or by wheels that are frozen in the mud, something else happens. Then the twisting force, unable to turn the wheels, will rotate the tractor around the axle.

Anytime it's easier for the engine to lift the front end of the tractor than it is to move the tractor forward or spin the wheels; the engine power will lift the front wheels off the ground. If the engine doesn't die, or the operator doesn't react immediately and step on the clutch, the tractor can rotate all the way over. Without a ROPS, the operator probably will be crushed.

If the tractor is stuck, never put boards or logs in front of the drive wheels thinking it will increase traction. If the drive wheels catch on them and cannot turn, the tractor may tip over backwards.

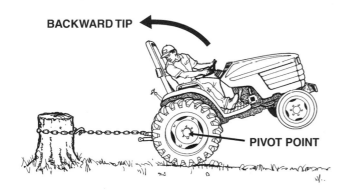

Fig. 13 – A Very Heavy Load can Cause a Rear Upset

Rear-axle toque will upset the tractor if rear wheels can't spin or move forward (Fig. 13).

PREVENTING ROLLOVERS TO THE REAR

We have covered the forces that usually cause rollovers to the rear. Here are some practical tips for preventing those forces from causing a tractor upset.

Hitch Loads Only to the Drawbar

The proper hitching points on tractors are the regular drawbar or the drawbar attachment that are available for the 3-point hitch. Attach a load anywhere else and you risk a backward tip.

Control the Height of 3-point Hitch Drawbars

If you use a 3-point hitch drawbar attachment (Fig. 14), use the 3-point hitch's height limiting control to keep drawbar at the proper height – about 13 to 17 inches above the ground (check your tractor's operators manual).

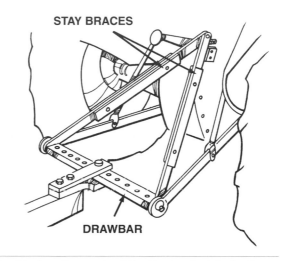

Fig. 14 – Stay Braces should be Used to Lock in the Proper Drawbar Height

On some compact tractors, stay braces should be used to lock in the proper drawbar height (Fig. 14). Without stay braces, the 3-point hitch could be accidentally raised, raising the hitch-point, and increasing the chance of a backward tip.

Have Your Tractor Properly Ballasted

Refer to your tractor's operators manual for the correct amount of **ballast**, or weight, to add to the tractor. If you raise the front wheels when you let out the clutch, chances are you need more front-end weight (Fig. 15).

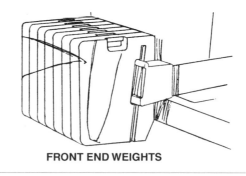

Fig. 15 – Front-end Weights can Limit the Chances of a Backward Tip

Start Forward Motion Slowly

Have the engine running at a slow speed and slowly release the clutch. If a backward tip should start, either the tractor engine will stall or the front end will lift slowly enough so you can react and put in the clutch.

Change Speeds Gradually

Quick accelerations when going up steep grades, or with a heavy load, can lift front wheels off the ground. Without the front wheels on the ground there is no steering control. It could also start a rearward upset.

Go Up Hills in Reverse, Go Down Hills in Forward

Many rearward upsets happen when tractors back or coast down a hill. Quickly braking, or quickly engaging the clutch, can cause the tractor's momentum to flip the tractor over backward. The steeper the grade, and the faster you are going, the more likely the upset. Always brake and clutch gently. Better yet, when driving up or down a hill, keep the front end of the tractor facing down hill.

Fig. 16 – Sudden Braking can Cause an Upset

Beware of coasting or backing down hills. Sudden braking, or clutching, can cause the tractor to flip over backward.

Plan for Safe Uphill Pulls

Pulling heavy loads uphill can be dangerous since the slope and drawbar leverage both work to tip the tractor backward. The safest procedure is to add front-end weights, set the drawbar at its lowest and strongest position, engage the clutch slowly, and accelerate gradually.

Avoid Ditches

Ditches, especially slippery ones, are a prescription for trouble. If you must cross them, recognize the hazards involved. When crossing a ditch make sure you drive forward when going downhill, and backward when going uphill. Use low gear and drive slowly. If the ditch is so steep or slippery that the tractor will slide, don't cross the ditch. You won't have the control to do it safely.

If Your Tractor gets Stuck in Mud – Back it Out

This may first require digging out mud behind the rear wheels and towing or winching out an implement. If backing out is impossible, dig mud away from the front of all tires, unhook any implements, and drive out forward.

CAUSES OF ROLLOVERS TO THE SIDE

Earlier we mentioned the forces usually involved in tractor upsets:

- **Leverage on the drawbar or hitch**
- **Rear-axle torque**
- **Centrifugal force**
- **Gravity**

While the first two forces play a major role in rearward upsets, the last two forces – centrifugal and gravity – are big factors in rollovers to the side. Side rollovers are the most common cause of tractor related injury and death.

FORCE 3: CENTRIFUGAL FORCE

Even if you didn't know it by name, centrifugal force is something you have felt. It's the sideways force you feel every time a car makes a sharp turn – the force that pushes you outward when you make a turn.

If you played crack-the-whip as a child, you may remember the high forces you felt if you were the kid at the end of the "whip."

Those same forces affect a turning tractor. If you turn a tractor sharp enough, and at a high enough speed, centrifugal force can actually be great enough to roll over a tractor.

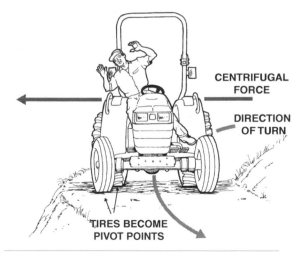

Fig. 17 – Centrifugal Force Tries to Pivot Tractor on its Outside Wheels

Both the speed and the sharpness of a turn play major roles in the amount of centrifugal force, and thus the likelihood of a tractor upset.

Centrifugal force varies in proportion to the square of the tractor's speed. That means increasing the speed greatly increases the centrifugal force.

For example, doubling the tractor's speed, from 5 to 10 miles per hour, increases the strength of the centrifugal force by four times (2 squared = 2 x 2 = 4). Tripling the speed, from 5 to 15 miles per hour, increases the strength of the centrifugal force nine times (3 squared = 3 x 3 = 9).

Centrifugal force also varies in reverse proportions to the turning radius. Make a turn twice as wide, and you cut the centrifugal force in half.

You probably can guess how to limit the chances of centrifugal force upsetting your tractor – turn wide and slow down.

FORCE 4: GRAVITY

Gravity is perhaps the most important force involved in tractor upsets. In those situations where gravity works for you, it acts to counter the other three forces to keep the tractor upright. However, on steep slopes gravity can work with other forces to help tip you over.

Gravity is the force the earth exerts on all things. Gravity gives us our weight, stability, and keeps our feet on the ground.

To understand how gravity works on all things, you need to understand the term **center of gravity**. The center of gravity – and all objects have one – is an imaginary point where all parts of an object balance one another. If you could suspend an object from that one point, it would balance perfectly. With a block of wood that's easy to imagine – it would be exactly in the center.

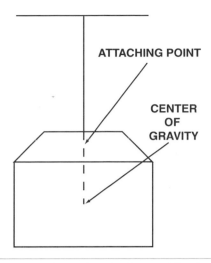

Fig. 18 – Suspend an Object from its Center of Gravity and it will Balance Perfectly

On a tractor, it's a bit more complicated. Its center of gravity is not in the middle of the tractor because heavy components like the transmission, rear axle, and rear tires are all in the rear of the tractor. That means the center of gravity is more to the rear of the tractor. Furthermore, since almost all components are above the rear axle, so is the center of gravity.

Fig. 19 – Center of Gravity on a Compact Tractor

The center of gravity is important because the force of gravity acts on an object as if all an object's weight were concentrated at one point – that point being the center of gravity. Gravity is blind as to what shape an object has; it acts as if all an object's weight were concentrated at the center of gravity.

BASE OF STABILITY

Another important concept in understanding tractor upsets is the **base of stability**. It is the base that supports an object, kind of like an object's footprint. On a block of wood, it's simply the size of the side of the block resting on the ground. On a tractor, the base of stability could be considered the distance between the rear wheels (Fig. 20).

If we tip the block a little, the weight swings toward the edge supporting the block. If the block is released, it will fall back to its original position. That's because the weight and the center of gravity remained within the base of stability. But, if we tip the block far enough, it will fall over on its side. The block will remain upright, only as long as the weight attached to the center of gravity, stays within its base of stability, the bottom edge of the block.

The same concepts and forces affect a tractor. As long as the pull of gravity, acting through the center of gravity stays within the base of stability (the tractor wheelbase) the tractor will stay upright. But if the tractor tips to the point that the center of gravity goes beyond the base of stability, the tractor will roll over (Fig. 22). Setting the tractor's rear wheels as wide apart as possible increases the tractor's base of stability and limits the chances to upset.

When it comes to tractor upsets; the force of gravity generally does not work alone. One or more of the other three forces – centrifugal, rear-axle torque, and leverage of the drawbar – can work with gravity to cause an upset.

For example, a tractor parked on a moderate slope will not overturn by itself. But if you make a fast turn on that same slope, the added push of centrifugal force could cause a rollover.

← BASE OF STABILTIY →

Fig. 20 – Base of Stability

To illustrate how center of gravity and base of stability affect each other, let's think again of a block of wood. Imagine we could attach a string and a weight to the block's center of gravity. The weight represents the pull of gravity.

Once the center of gravity moves outside the base of stability, the block will flip over on its side (Fig. 21).

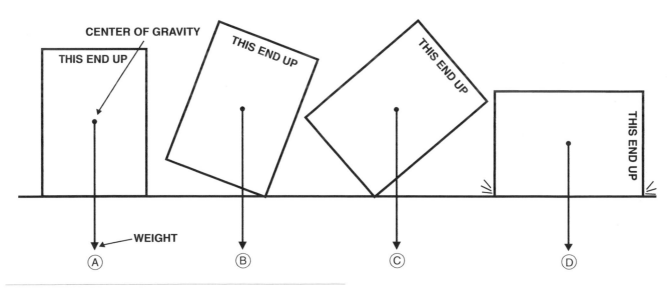

Fig. 21 – How Center of Gravity and Base of Stability Affect Each Other

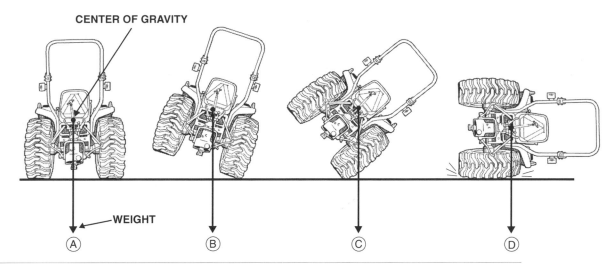

Fig. 22 – As with the Block, if the Center of Gravity Moves Outside the Base of Stability the Tractor will Roll Over

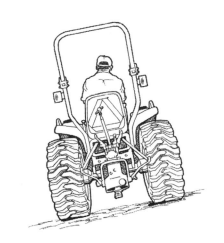

This Could Be You...No one knows exactly how it happened. Noah had been mowing that same driveway every summer Saturday since he had retired. Why was today different? It certainly wasn't the tractor. Noah had bought it new himself some 35 years ago, when he started his landscaping business. Was it that gopher hole? Did an insect distract him? Or did he turn around to check the rotary cutter and just drift into the ditch? At least it probably happened fast. One second you're mowing along the driveway, the next second you're at the bottom of a ditch, crushed to death. Without a ROPS, Noah didn't have much of a chance.

PREVENTING ROLLOVERS TO THE SIDE

We've discussed the forces that cause rollovers to the side. Now that we better understand those forces, let's look at what tractor operators should do to prevent those forces from causing a tractor upset.

Choose a Wide Wheel Spacing
Setting the rear wheels as far apart as possible increases your tractor's base of stability.

Turn Slowly
Remember that centrifugal force affects the stability of your tractor. Chances of tipping are greatest when crossing slopes and while turning uphill. But tractors can also tip when turning on level ground. To prevent upsets, drive slowly and turn wide.

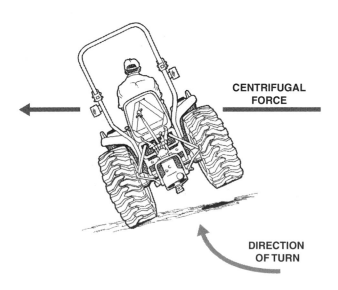

Fig. 23 – A Tractor Parked on a Slope may be Stable. But, Make an Uphill Turn on that Same Slope and the Addition of Centrifugal Force can Cause an Upset.

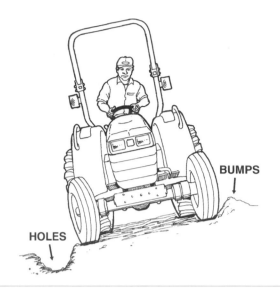

Fig. 24 – *Watch for Bumps and Holes that might Upset the Tractor*

Avoid Crossing Steep Slopes

Tractor stability is reduced on steep slopes. If you must cross a steep slope, drive slowly and avoid quick uphill turns. Also watch for holes or depressions on the downhill side, and for bumps or obstructions on the uphill side. Space rear wheels far apart to increase stability.

Operate Front End-loaders Cautiously

Attachments affect a tractor's center of gravity. A raised loader can significantly raise a tractor's center of gravity, making it less stable. Keep the loader bucket as low as possible when turning and transporting. Avoid quick starts, stops and turns.

Fig. 25 – *Keep Loader Bucket as Low as Possible when Turning and Transporting*

Are you Using that Loader?

If the loader is not needed for the task, it is better that it be removed and safely parked. For more on loader safety, see Chapter 6.

Restrict Your Speed

Slowing down gives you more time to react to changing terrain or hazards in your path.

Lock Brakes Together during Transport

Braking only one rear wheel will send most, or all, engine power to the other rear wheel. At transport speeds this can swerve the tractor abruptly right or left and into a rollover situation (Fig. 26 and 27).

Fig. 26 – *Always Lock Brakes together when Operating a Tractor at Transport Speeds*

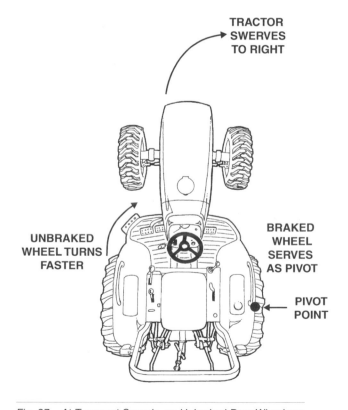

Fig. 27 – *At Transport Speeds, an Unbraked Rear Wheel can Swerve a Tractor Out of Control*

Don't Let Your Tractor Bounce

A tractor bouncing could cause loss of steering control. Slow down to avoid bouncing.

Drive Slowly in Slippery Conditions

If your tractor starts to skid sideways, you have lost full control. If the tires hit an obstruction or surface that suddenly stops the tires, your tractor could roll over.

Pull Heavy Loads and Equipment at Safe Speeds

Heavy loads put an added strain on your tractor's brakes, greatly increasing stopping distance. Slow down well before you need to stop. Slow the engine down early and gently step on the brakes (Fig. 28).

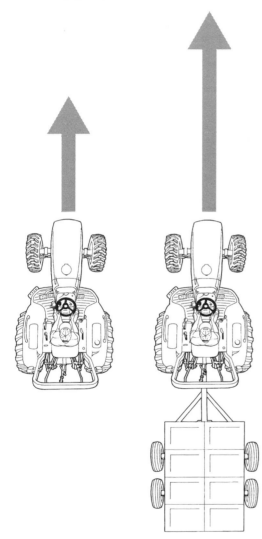

Fig. 28 — Heavy Loads Greatly Increase Stopping Distance

Beware of Ditches and River Banks

Stay at least as far away from the bank as the ditch is deep. That's because the weight of a tractor could cave the bank in as you cross or approach the shear line. As you approach ditches or banks, look ahead rather than at an implement. Stay alert and watch for holes, gullies, and washouts that could place your tractor in an unstable position (Fig. 29).

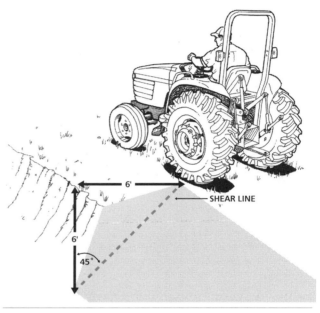

Fig. 29 – Always Keep Your Tractor Beyond the Shear Line when Operating near Ditches and Banks

Use Engine Braking Power when Going Downhill

Runaway tractors often upset. Shift to a lower gear and reduce speed for downhill travel. Shift before you start downhill. If you have already started accelerating, you may not be able to downshift.

 SAFETY ALERT: Some tractors "freewheel" and provide no engine braking in certain speed ranges. Check your operator manual. Understand the transmission before you drive the tractor.

REMEMBER, ROPS SAVES LIVES

While it is good to understand what causes tractor upsets, and how to recognize potential hazardous situations, the most foolproof way to escape an injury is to be protected by a ROPS. Remember the odds in case of an upset. Without a ROPS, there is a 75% chance that the operator will not survive a rollover. If the tractor has a ROPS and the operator wears the seatbelt, there is a 95% chance of the operator walking away from a tractor upset.

Fig. 30 – Always Wear your Seatbelt when Operating a Tractor with ROPS

RUNOVERS

Each year many people are killed or seriously injured when they are run over by a tractor. Many of these victims are children. Virtually all of these incidents could be easily avoided.

RIDER INJURIES
One major group of run-over victims is riders who fall off a tractor or implement. All tractor operators need to have a simple rule – no extra riders. Tractors are not people movers. If there isn't an approved extra seat, there shouldn't be a rider.

Fig. 31 – If there isn't a Seat, there shouldn't be a Rider

Extra passengers do more than endanger their own safety when they ride along on tractors or equipment. Since there is no room for extra riders on most tractors, they often end up leaning against or sitting on controls. This can cause surprises in tractor operation that can have deadly results.

Tractors are work vehicles, not people movers. Extra riders make it more difficult for the operator to safely drive the tractor. Never allow riders on tractors or attachments.

BYPASS STARTING
Modern tractors have interlock systems that make it impossible to start a tractor when one or more potential safety hazards are present. These potential hazards include:

- **the tractor is in gear**
- **the clutch isn't fully depressed**
- **the PTO is engaged**
- **the operator isn't in the tractor seat.**

While these systems are in place to protect the operator, they can be disabled or bypassed. Bypass starting is attempting to start a tractor by bypassing these safety interlock systems.

One common way operators attempt to bypass start on a tractor is by shorting across the terminals on the starter. Never try to start a tractor by shorting across the starter terminals (Fig. 32). If the tractor is in gear, it could lunge forward and crush you. This has been a major cause of death and injuries.

Fig. 32 – Never Try to Start a Tractor by Shorting Across the Starter Terminals

If the tractor is in gear, it will spring to life suddenly and lurch on top of the person doing the bypass starting. The only safe place to be when you start your tractor is in the tractor seat.

Some people mistakenly think they can just jump out of the way if the tractor is in gear. If doesn't work that way. Many modern tractors have hydraulic clutches that don't engage until the tractor engine powers up the hydraulic system.

This can mean, even if the tractor is in gear, the wheels won't move as the engine starts turning over.

Many bypass-start victims have thought their tractor was in neutral or park, when actually there simply wasn't enough hydraulic pressure for the clutch to engage. But once the tractor starts, and the engine reaches approximately 1,000 rpms, hydraulic pressure will suddenly engage the clutch. Before you know it, the tractor lunges forward and is on top of you.

Never try to start a tractor unless you are sitting in the tractor seat. If safety interlock devices have been tampered with or are broken, get them repaired. They exist for a reason – to prevent injuries and save lives.

BYSTANDER INJURIES

Another group of people who can become victims of tractor run-overs are bystanders. Sometimes the victim may be a co-worker who the tractor operator knew was in the general area, but didn't see. Sometimes it's a surprise visitor, such as an inquisitive child or client who comes to see the operator.

The way to prevent this type of incident is for the operator to be attentive to everything near the tractor.

Before starting, it's a good idea to walk completely around the tractor and implement to make sure no one is near the equipment. Also sound the horn or yell, "starting" to warn those in the area that the equipment is about to move. Never run up to an operating tractor (Fig. 33). Wait a safe distance until you can get the operator's attention. Then wait until the tractor has been shut off.

Fig. 33 – Never Run up to an Operating Tractor

Make sure co-workers and clients know never to sneak up on equipment. They should know to keep a safe distance until they can get your attention and shut down the machine.

FALLS

Falls are another cause of serious injuries. Most often falls happen while mounting or dismounting the tractor. Here are some good rules to prevent falls off of tractors:

Keep Steps and Platforms Clean and Dry
Take time to clean off mud, ice, grease, and other debris that can accumulate on the platform and steps.

Don't Store Log Chains or Tool Boxes on Steps or Platforms
These items make it difficult to safely get on and off the tractor. Plus, they can slide around hindering your ability to use tractor controls.

Fig. 34 – Most Falls Occur While Mounting and Dismounting the Tractor

Use Handrails and/or Handholds
Handrails and handholds are there to give you more control while mounting and dismounting the tractor.

Face the Tractor
Face the tractor when you are mounting and dismounting.

Never Jump from the Tractor
Dismount the tractor the same way you mounted. Never jump from the tractor.

Never Dismount while the Tractor is Coasting

Get on and off the tractor only after it has come to a full stop and you have shut off the engine.

Only Operate the Tractor from the Tractor Seat

That may sound obvious, but every year operators fall or are bounced off their tractors because they used a fender, a step, or a drawbar as an operator's platform. Stay in the seat with your seatbelt buckled while you are operating the tractor.

HITCHING MISHAPS

Whenever an operator is hitching equipment up to a tractor, there is an increased chance for an injury.

If the operator is performing the job alone he may have to get on and off the tractor several times to properly line up the attachment and the tractor. It's not uncommon for an operator in this situation to take a short cut and try to manually move either the tractor or the attachment into position. (The tractor's 3-point hitch attaches to an implement at three points (Fig. 35). Power to the implement comes via the tractor's PTO.)

If a second party is helping, there's the chance that the helper will get crushed between the moving tractor and the stationary attachment. Watch where you stand when you help hook up an attachment to a tractor. It is dangerous to stand between the tractor and an attachment while the tractor is in reverse.

Fig. 36 – It's Dangerous to Stand Between the Tractor and an Implement while the Tractor is in Reverse

Here are some good safety tips to make hitching up safer:

Move the Tractor only from the Tractor Seat

Never attempt to operate the tractor from the ground. The risk of getting pinned is too great.

Never Pull or Push the Tractor

Turn the engine off and shift into park, or set the parking brake before dismounting. This precaution is especially important on sloping ground. Pulling or pushing the tractor to align it with the attachment could bring it rolling toward you with crushing force.

Telescope Links when Attaching 3-point Hitches

Telescoping lower links, found on some 3-point hitch systems, simplify attaching (Fig. 37). A release button lets the end of the link slide out slightly to aid alignment with the implement. Once the implement is attached, the operator backs up to lock the tractor link into operating position.

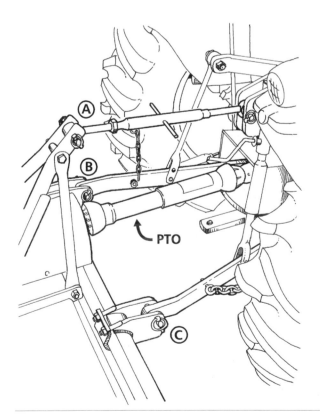

Fig. 35 – The Tractor's 3-Point Hitch attaches to an Implement at Three Points: A, B, and C

Fig. 37 – Telescoping Links

Protect Your Helper

Shift to park or set the parking brake before permitting a helper to go between the tractor and the implement. If you must move the tractor to align the hitch, back the tractor past the hitch alignment point, and shift to forward before your helper steps in. Then complete the hook-up with the tractor moving forward. This eliminates the risk of crushing your partner between the tractor and the attachment if your foot slips off the clutch.

Helpers Stand Aside

If you are helping hitch, never stand behind a tractor when it is backing up – stand to the side. Let the driver align the hitch and put the tractor in park or a forward gear. Then stop in and make the attachment.

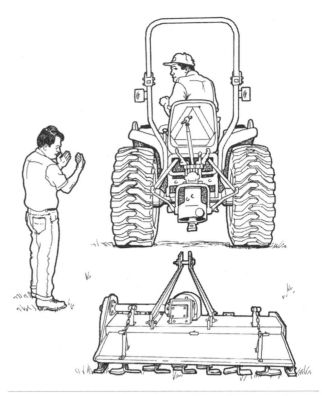

Fig. 38 – Helpers should Stand Aside while the Tractor is in Reverse

Beware of Load-sensing 3-point Hitches

If a tractor has a load sensing 3-point hitch, be sure the control lever is positioned to maintain a set hitch height. If the tractor's 3-point hitch control is set for load-sensing position, the sudden load of attaching an implement may cause the hitch arms to raise unexpectedly. Check your operator manual.

Block up an Implement's Tongue

By blocking up the implement's tongue, the operator can better align the hitch holes with the tractors.

Fig. 39 – Block up the Implement's Tongue

Use Hitch Pins with a Locking Device

Locking devices prevent the hitch pin from jumping out and releasing the trailed equipment. Use hitch pins that have a locking device to keep them in place. Bent or damaged hitch pins should be replaced.

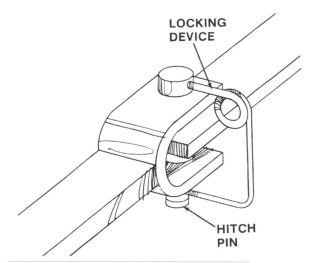

Fig. 40 – Use Hitch Pins that have Locking Devices

Properly Store Equipment

Equipment is easier to hook up if it is properly stored in the first place. Select a firm, level, and well-drained location. Be sure the equipment is properly supported – that all jack stands are lowered, and wheels are blocked. Some attachments may not be balanced when uncoupled from the tractor, so extra blocking may be needed to make some equipment stable.

POWER TAKE-OFF ENTANGLEMENTS

The power take-off (PTO) is a convenient and safe way to transmit tractor power to an implement or attachment. This power is transmitted at high speeds – typically 540 rpms for rear PTO's and 2,000 rmps for mid PTO's. Because of these high speeds and the fact that the PTO transmits engine power, the PTO is a potential hazard that must be respected. Compact tractors typically have a rear PTO to power rear attachments. A mid PTO (top photo, Fig. 41) powers mid-mount and front attachments.

Fig. 41 – Rear PTO and Mid PTO

New tractors and new PTO-drive equipment come from the factory with shielding that offers excellent protection. The real safety hazards come if shields become damaged, modified, or discarded. In fact, a Purdue University study of PTO-related injuries showed that nearly 90% of entanglements occurred where the PTO shielding was missing or damaged.

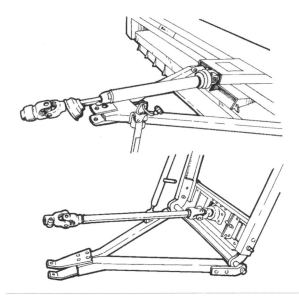

Fig. 42 – Damaged or Missing PTO Shields are Very Dangerous
and Must be Repaired or Replaced

An unguarded PTO, or one with damaged shields, is very dangerous (Fig. 42). It can catch on your clothing and pull you into the spinning shaft. A PTO shaft turning at the standard speed of 540 rpms can tear and entangle clothing at the rate of five to seven feet per second. Sometimes it takes only a loose thread, or dangling drawstring to drag you into a life-threatening situation. It happens too fast to react, and the tractor power is too strong to overcome. In an instant, you could be strangled, mutilated, or killed.

Here are some safety rules to keep that from happening:

Keep all Shields in Place

Tractors usually have a master PTO shield around the PTO stub. Never tamper with or remove this shield. It protects you from the spinning universal join and PTO shaft. To prevent injuries, keep tractor PTO shields in place and in good condition (Fig. 43).

Fig. 43 – Keep Tractor PTO Shields in Place and in Good Condition

Check that Integral Shields can Rotate Freely

Most PTO shafts are protected with a shield. This shield is a metal or plastic tube supported by bearings so it can rotate independently of the shaft. Thus if you should happen to bump or fall into the shield while it is rotating; it will stop moving, even as the shaft inside the shield continues to rotate. When power is shut off, you should be able to rotate the shield freely by hand. If you have trouble rotating the shield, the bearings may be damaged and the shield must be repaired.

Replace Damaged PTO Shields

Most machines will continue to operate with damaged shields, but they won't operate safely. Replace any damaged shields before they can contribute to a serious injury.

Never Step Across a Rotating Powershaft

When PTO-driven machines are running, always walk around the machine. Safety devices could malfunction, so it's not worth the risk.

Wear Snug-fitting Clothing and Short or Restrained Hair

When around PTO-drive equipment, always wear snug-fitting clothing and have short or restrained hair. Anything loose or flowing – scarves, drawstrings on jackets, long hair, frayed clothing, dangling necklaces or earrings – can get wrapped on PTO's and other rotating components. Many victims have been severely injured, handicapped, and disfigured. Dress safely and avoid such tragedies.

COLLISIONS WITH MOTOR VEHICLES

Most motorists have lots of experience driving behind fast-moving vehicles, but relatively little experience driving behind slow-moving vehicles. Thus, if you drive a tractor on public roads, you have a major responsibility to help motorists avoid hitting you. It's for your own protection – and theirs.

WHY THE SMV SIGN?

The best way to alert automobile and truck drivers that you are going slowly is to properly display a slow-moving vehicle (SMV) emblem whenever you travel on a public road.

Fig. 44 – Slow-Moving Vehicle (SMV) Emblem

The triangular SMV emblem is the universal symbol that tells drivers behind you that you are traveling at 25 mph or less (Fig. 44). State law throughout most of the United States requires it. Also, federal regulations (OSHA) require SMV emblems on machines operated by employees.

Most new tractors and implements come equipped from the factory with SMV emblems. If you need to add an emblem on your machinery, mount it at the rear toward the center from 2 to 6 ft. above the ground with the point at the top (Fig. 45). If the point is downward, the emblem will not look like the universal symbol. The SMV emblem should always give every motorist the same message.

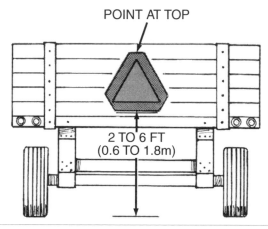

Fig. 45 – Always Mount the SMV Emblem with the Point at the Top

Keep the emblem surface clean and in good condition for day and night identification. Over time, SMV emblems will fade and lose their effectiveness. When the reflective red border or fluorescent orange center has lost its brilliance, the emblem should be replaced. If motorists can't see the emblem clearly, it offers no protection.

There is another reason to renew the SMV's on your equipment...In 1997, a new and brighter SMV was introduced. These SMV signs use a retro-reflective material that is as much as 10 times brighter than material previously used in SMV emblems. Plus these new emblems maintain their brightness longer.

These retro-reflective emblems are available in a self-stick form for applying to existing SMV emblems. It is a good idea to have all equipment purchased prior to 1997 restickered. (Contact your equipment dealer or Gemplers, Inc. at 1-800-382-8473). Mount the emblem securely and always with the point to the top.

The SMV is not a substitute for warning lights and reflectors. Lights make your equipment visible, while the emblem tells motorists you are moving slowly. Consult your local and state laws for regulations.

FOLLOW RULES OF THE ROAD

When driving a tractor on the road, occupy a full lane of the highway – it is the safest position. You have every right to be there. Do not drive partially on the road and partially on the shoulder. This only encourages motorists to pass in unsafe situations. Driving on the shoulder also poses special risks. If you suddenly see an obstruction on the shoulder and have to swerve back onto the road, you could cause a serious safety hazard.

If traffic backs up behind you, and there is a smooth wide shoulder, you can pull off onto the shoulder, stop, and let the vehicles pass. You have no obligation to get off the road, so pull off only if you are sure you can do it safely on a clear, level shoulder.

Fig. 46 – You can pull off on to the Shoulder to let Cars Pass

Don't encourage motorists to take chances. Signaling them to pass is risky. The traffic situation could change so quickly that they might not be able to pass safely.

Obey all traffic signs. Even though you are driving a slow-moving vehicle, traffic rules still apply. Other drivers (as well as the traffic police) will expect tractor operators to stop and yield just like any other vehicle.

Newer tractors are equipped with turn signals. Use them if your tractor has them. If not, use standard hand signals to warn others you are going to stop or turn (Fig. 47). Remember that towed equipment may obstruct the vision of drivers behind you. If so, they won't be able to see your signals. Take extra caution.

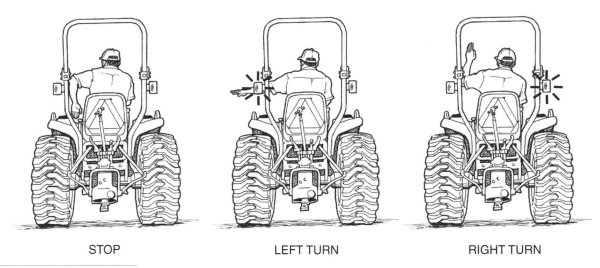

STOP   LEFT TURN   RIGHT TURN

Fig. 47 – Standard Hand Signals

BRAKING MAY TAKE LONGER

Higher speeds lengthen braking distance and time. Slow down before braking. This uses engine power to reduce your speed before you apply the brakes. Tow heavy loads at less than road-gear speeds. **Always lock brake pedals together so there is equal braking pressure on each wheel.**

Pump the brakes when trying to stop on slippery surfaces like ice, snow or mud. If the tractor skids when brakes are applied, release them and apply them again with a slight pumping action – on and off – until the tractor stops.

When towing an implement, attach a safety chain between the tractor and the implement. The safety chain will control the implement if the hitch pin fails for any reason. If an implement doesn't have a safety chain, contact your equipment dealer for one that's the proper size for your machine.

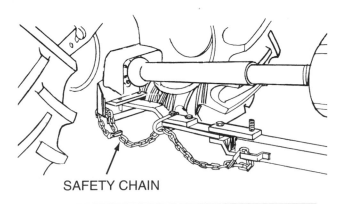

SAFETY CHAIN

Fig. 48 – Safety Chains Help Control the Implement if the Hitch Pin Fails

HYDRAULIC HAZARDS

Tractor hydraulic systems generate very high pressures, in excess of 2,000 psi. Water in a typical home has a pressure more like 40 psi. Not only is the pressure in a tractor hydraulic system much greater than anything we normally encounter, buy hydraulic fluid itself poses a serious health risk.

PINHOLE LEAKS

High pressure sprays from pinhole leaks can penetrate human skin, flesh, and eyes and cause serious health risks. If any fluid is injected into the skin, a doctor familiar with this type of injury must surgically remove it within a few hours. If the injury isn't treated, gangrene may result.

To make matters worse, these pinhole leaks can be very hard to detect. You may see only the symptoms of pinhole leaks. There may appear to be only dripping of fluid, when actually those drops are the accumulations of fluid from a high-pressure spray so fine it is invisible.

This Could Be You...Before she could get back to work, Rose just had to get those tangled weeds cleared from the rear tiller. It shouldn't take long. Rose had left the rear tiller attachment raised up when she got off the tractor. That way she could get under the tiller better, to pull at the weeds. She was making good progress when Bill walked up. Hydraulic pressure was the furthest thing from Rose's mind when she asked Bill to get a screwdriver from the tractor toolbox. She thought only about the wrapped mass of weeds. It never crossed her mind that Bill would bump the tractor's hydraulic lever as he searched for the screwdriver. After the incident, with two broken legs and a crushed knee, Rose had plenty of time to think about what had gone terribly wrong.

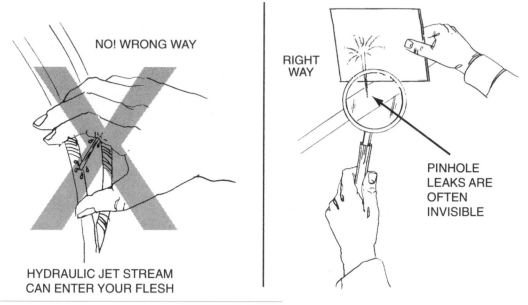

Fig. 49 – Use a Piece of Cardboard or Wood to Check for Hydraulic Leaks

Never try to locate a leak by touching a wet hose with a bare or even a gloved hand. Instead, wear safety glasses and pass a piece of cardboard or wood over the suspected area. Relieve pressure before correcting the leak.

SUDDEN PRESSURE RELEASE

The high pressures generated by a tractor's hydraulic system enables the tractor to lift and hold up heavy objects and attachments. If this pressure is suddenly released the heavy object or attachment will come crashing to the ground. Never leave the tractor with an attachment raised. A hydraulic failure or a simple bump of a hydraulic lever could cause a serious injury.

Fig. 50 – Never Work Under a Raised Attachment or Leave the Tractor with an Attachment Raised

While this sudden release of pressure can happen from a failure in the hydraulic system, it more commonly takes place when the tractor is shut off and the hydraulic lever is bumped.

If the hydraulic control lever is moved while the tractor is shut off, hydraulic oil pressure will be released. That's why it's so important to lower all attachments before dismounting the tractor.

After the tractor is shut off, cycle the 3-point hitch and any other hydraulic control levers several times. This will assure that all hydraulic pressure has been released and that attachments are safely on the ground.

For more information on potential hydraulic hazards, see Chapter 3.

TOWING DISABLED EQUIPMENT

If you have a tractor, chances are one day you will be asked to tow a disabled or stuck vehicle. This can be a risky proposition, so understand the hazards before you start.

KEEP ENGINE RUNNING

Remember if the machine to be towed has power steering and brakes it should not be pulled unless its engine is running. The engine is needed to provide hydraulic power to the steering and brake systems.

If you use a chain to pull another vehicle, select one long enough to give the driver of the towed vehicle enough stopping time and distance to avoid a rear-end collision with your tractor.

When towing with a chain, never snap the chain tight. This can snap the chain in two. Pull it tight – slowly. Only after the chain is tight should you fully release the clutch and power up the tractor engine.

Nylon ropes have become popular towing tools in recent years. They also can be a deadly. Nylon rope stretches under load, storing huge amounts of energy, much like a slingshot.

If a hook or clevis on one end of a nylon rope breaks, that end of the rope, along with any remaining pieces of metal, will be propelled toward the other end of the rope at speeds that can approach 500 mph. That means rope and metal come flying toward one of the vehicles at the speed of a missile. Every year, flying nylon ropes are the cause of deaths.

If you do use nylon rope to pull:

- **make sure it is overrated for the type of towing job.**

- **use the hooks provided with the tow rope. Attaching other clevises or hooks increases the chance of metal failure and serious injuries.**

- **go very slowly until the rope is tight, and only then increase speed.**

- **never drive fast, hoping the stretch of the rope will help pull out the stuck vehicle. This is extremely dangerous and a major cause of rope failures and serious injuries.**

Be sure the hitch point on the disabled vehicle is strong enough for towing and located as close as possible to its centerline. Never hitch to any steering linkage – it is not strong enough and will probably bend.

The drawbar of the towing tractor is the only place to attach a towing device. Attaching it higher could risk a tractor upset, as was explained earlier in this chapter.

Make sure both operators know the plan for starting and stopping. Once you are both on/in your vehicles, the two of you will not be able to talk. Decide on hand signals before you start towing.

PARKING A TRACTOR

When you are done operating a tractor, your final task is to properly park it. It doesn't matter if you are stopping for the day, or just a few minutes, it's important to follow proper parking procedures.

DON'T GET OFF A RUNNING TRACTOR
Put the tractor in Park, and/or set the parking brake. Turn off the engine and all electrical switches.

Once the tractor is shut off, it's important to release any hydraulic pressure. This generally means lowering all equipment and attachments to the ground.

Never rely on the tractor's hydraulic system to support a raised implement or attachment, even for just a short time. Hydraulic lines can rupture, and seals and valves may fail. Any such failure would cause an attachment to suddenly drop.

Fig. 51 – Nylon Ropes can Break, Hurling Rope and Parts at Towed Vehicle

Fig. 52 – Always Lower Attachments when Getting off the Tractor

Plus, if attachments are not lowered to the ground, children or others could accidentally bump controls. Even with the tractor shut off, moving the hydraulic lever can send attachments crashing to the ground.

The operator's final task is to remove the key. Taking the key keeps children or unauthorized people from starting and moving the tractor. While theft is certainly one concern, the greater risk is generally that a young and inexperienced operator will try out the tractor, hurting themselves and/or others.

ADDITIONAL RESOURCES:

Farm and Ranch Safety Management, Deere & Company, John Deere Publishing, Moline, IL

Agricultural Tractor Safety Manual, Equipment Manufacturers Institute, Chicago, IL

WEBSITES:

There's lots of safety-related information and links at the National Ag Safety Database:
www.cdc.gov/niosh/nasd/nasdhome.html

TEST YOURSELF

QUESTIONS - CHAPTER 5

1. How does a ROPS save lives?

2. To be protected by a ROPS, what must you always do?

3. What is the danger of towing with a nylon rope?

4. How does centrifugal force influence tractor rollovers?

5. What two important things can you do to prevent a rollover?

6. Name three things you can do to prevent PTO entanglements.

LOADERS, BACKHOE ATTACHMENTS AND SKID-STEER LOADERS

6

Fig. 1 – Loader Attached to Front of Tractor; Backhoe Attached to Rear

INTRODUCTION

Part of the usefulness of compact tractors is that they work with many different attachments. Two of the most popular attachments are loaders and backhoes. Loaders are attached to the front of a tractor and backhoes are attached to the rear (Fig. 1). They use a tractor's hydraulic power to dig, lift, and move material.

These attachments add two special safety concerns for tractor operators. First, both loaders and backhoes have moving parts and crush points that can cause injury. Second, adding a loader or a backhoe to a tractor can greatly change a tractor's stability and handling. To be a safe operator, you'll need to understand these changes.

Many of the safety concerns with loaders and backhoes are also concerns on skid-steer loaders. We'll include these machines in our discussions.

Fig. 2 – Skid-steer Loader

Skid-steer loaders maneuver by changing speed and/or direction of drive wheels on either side of the machine. This allows "skid steers" to turn sharply and spin in a tight circle.

IMPORTANT SAFETY CONCERNS

Most mishaps with loaders, backhoes, and skid-steer loaders can be divided into three broad categories:

- **Rollovers**
- **Injuries to helpers**
- **Injuries to operators.**

Let's look at each of these safety concerns to understand how injuries can be prevented.

ROLLOVERS

Any time a loader, backhoe, or skid steer lifts weight up into the air its center of gravity also rises. The higher you lift the weight, the higher goes the machine's center of gravity, and the easier it is for the vehicle to tip over. (See discussion of center of gravity and base of stability in Chapter 5.)

Even lifting an empty bucket raises the center of gravity and decreases a vehicle's stability (Fig. 3).

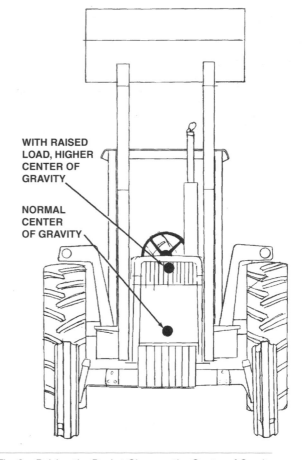

WITH RAISED LOAD, HIGHER CENTER OF GRAVITY

NORMAL CENTER OF GRAVITY

Fig. 3 – Raising the Bucket Changes the Center of Gravity

When a machine is standing still, a higher center of gravity is not a big concern. But start driving around with a load up in the air, and you have greatly increased the chance for a rollover.

The first safety rule of operating any loader is to keep the bucket low whenever you are driving. Keeping the load low not only limits the stress on the loader frame; it also keeps the center of gravity low limiting your chance of a rollover.

Driving slowly is also very important. As you learned in Chapter 5, the higher a vehicle's speed, the higher the centrifugal force and the greater the chance of upset. Keep your speed down and your load low and you greatly reduce your risk of rollover.

The density of the material you are hauling will also have an impact on the tractor's or skid steer's handling characteristics. Haul a bucketful of sawdust and you may not even notice you have a load. Haul the same volume of wet sand and everything changes. Thus the heavier your load, the greater your caution should be.

Buckets should be loaded evenly from side to side, especially when hauling dense materials. An evenly loaded bucket will evenly distribute the weight across the width of the tractor that will also help prevent upsets.

The capacity of your loader or skid steer is specified in the operator's manual. By following these recommendations you will extend machine life and make yourself a safer operator.

It's Time to Dump

When it's time to dump your load, keep the bucket as low as possible for as long as possible. For example, if you are going to dump a bucketful of gravel into a truck, keep the bucket low until you are almost to the truck (Fig. 4). Then raise the load and drive slowly forward to make your dump (Fig. 5).

Fig. 4 – Keep Bucket Low as You Approach the Truck

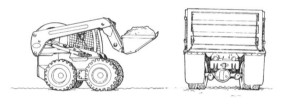

Fig. 5 – Slow Way Down as you Raise the Bucket

Once the bucket is high enough, drive into position and dump your load (Fig. 6).

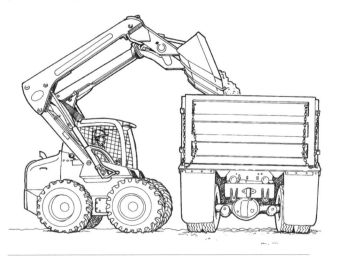

Fig. 6 – Drive Slowly Forward Once Bucket is High Enough and Dump your Load

Hills

Working on a hill will increase the chance of a rollover. If you must drive with a loaded bucket on a hill, go uphill in forward and downhill in reverse (Fig. 7). Avoid traveling or turning on side slopes.

Use extra care when operating any loader on rough ground. Bumps and dips increase the chance of an upset.

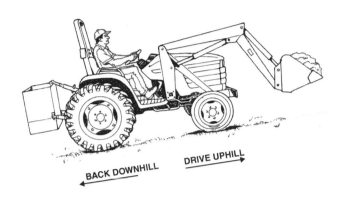

Fig. 7 – If You Must Drive a Loader on a Slope, Go Uphill in Forward and Downhill in Reverse

Ballast

Use the recommended amount of **ballast**. This is especially important with compact tractors. With a tractor-mounted loader on the front, rear ballast is needed to maintain good traction. With a backhoe attachment, front "ballast" is important. Many compact tractors require a loader be attached to help counterbalance the weight of the backhoe. This improves stability while using the backhoe and steering control during transport. If you remove the backhoe, you will have to add the rear ballast before you use the tractor loader. Check your operator's manual.

For loader and backhoe work, set tractor wheels at the widest recommended width. This gives you extra stability and helps prevent tractor upsets. Again, check the operator's manuals for specific recommendations.

INJURIES TO HELPERS

Whether you are planting trees or distributing mulch or moving dirt, it's not uncommon for helpers to be near an operating loader. This brings about special safety concerns for both the operator and the helper.

If helpers are going to be nearby, lower the bucket to the ground first (Fig. 8). And never allow anyone near or under a raised loader. An accidental bump of a hydraulic lever could send the loader down on the helper, even if the tractor is shut off (Chap. 5 Fig. 50).

Fig. 8 – Whenever Helpers are Near, Make Sure the Loader has been Lowered to the Ground

Whenever you get off the tractor, lower the bucket to the ground, shut off the engine, and remove the key. This way children or others can't accidentally lower the loader. If it is necessary to work on a loader in the raised position (repairs or maintenance), block it up securely so it absolutely cannot fall.

No Riders

Never allow riders on the tractor or on the loader. Riders could fall off or be bounced out of the loader while the tractor is moving. There usually is not enough time to stop the tractor before these fallen riders are run over.

Do not use front-end loaders as work platforms. Bumping controls could dump out your helpers and their tools.

 SAFETY ALERT: Be aware of overhead and underground electrical wires. Check overhead clearance. Also check underground utility locations before digging. (Call your local gas or electric supplier for help in finding buried wires and pipes.) If the machinery contacts electrical wires, stay in the seat. The tractor tires will protect you from electric shock. Back the machine away to get free of any wires. If you cannot free yourself, stay on the tractor until help arrives. Keep people away from the tractor until the power can be shut off. Even though you are safe sitting on the tractor, others who touch the tractor while standing on the ground could be electrocuted.

INJURIES TO OPERATORS

Since front-end loaders affect tractor stability, it is especially important that a loader tractor be equipped with a ROPS (Rollover Protective Structure). Do not operate a tractor that does not have rollover protection.

This is also true with skid-steer loaders. Modern skid-steer loaders are equipped with ROPS and a seat belt, as well as overhead protection against falling objects. Side screens keep the operator from reaching into the area where lift arms could crush or shear an arm, and they protect the operator from falling objects. A skid-steer operator needs to be protected from rollovers and falling objects. Keep all safety devices in place.

Fig. 9 – Keep All Safety Devices in Place

If the skid steer you will be operating does not have these safety devices, get the machine repaired immediately. Contact your equipment dealer or the machine's manufacturer for repair information. A skid-steer loader without a ROPS and safety side screens is a dangerous machine.

Only operate a loader, skid steer, or backhoe while sitting in the seat. Operating the controls from the ground or from behind the tractor could result in an operator getting crushed or entangled in the mechanisms. As lift arms move up and down next to the vehicle, they create several pinch points and crush points that can cause serious injuries.

Load Rollback

Load rollback is another serious hazard to the loader operator. Rollback happens when an unsecured load is lifted up and it spills out the back of the bucket. If the load is dirt, the result is just a dirty tractor. But if the load consists of large objects like barrels or landscape timbers, the consequences are much more serious. These objects could roll back down the loader arms onto the operator, causing injury or death (Fig. 10).

You can prevent this by properly securing your load and using the recommended materials-handling attachments. Follow your loader manufacturer's recommendations.

This Could Be You...Max felt so smart. Instead of having to wheelbarrow those cement blocks he would borrow the loader tractor. He could stack the bucket full of the blocks and get the whole job done in one trip. Everything was going according to plan until it was time to unload the blocks. Max had to drive through a tight spot in the storage area and the loader bucket blocked the view. So Max raised the bucket up as he inched forward. He was on solid ground and driving slowly so he had no fear of an upset. Suddenly an avalanche of cement blocks came raining down onto the tractor. One bounced down the loader arm and smashed onto Max's hand. Another just missed his head. In an instant it was all over. There were pieces of broken cement blocks scattered everywhere, the tractor had several big dents, and blood was pouring from Max's right hand. He was going to have some explaining to do.

Hydraulics

Loaders, backhoes, and skid steers all depend on high-pressure hydraulics. You need to be on the lookout for signs of hydraulic leaks. Loose connectors can be easy to spot. But some leaks, like pinhole leaks, can be very hard to detect. You may see only the symptoms of pinhole leaks. There may appear to be only hydraulic fluid dripping from some machine component, when actually those drops are the accumulation of fluid from a high-pressure spray so fine it is invisible.

Fig. 10 —Be Sure Loads are Properly Secured and can't Roll Back

Use extreme care if you spot a leak. A high-pressure stream of escaping hydraulic fluid can penetrate human skin and eyes. If any fluid is injected into the skin, a doctor familiar with this type of injury must surgically remove it within a few hours. If the injury isn't treated gangrene may result.

Never try to locate a leak by touching a wet hose with a bare or even a gloved hand. Instead, wear safety glasses and pass a piece of cardboard or wood over the suspected area. Relieve pressure before correcting the leak.

When attaching a loader or backhoe to a tractor, make sure hydraulic hoses are coupled to the proper tractor outlet. The loader must lift when you move the control to the "lift" position. If it doesn't respond properly, the unexpected action could cause property damage or an injury. Check your operator's manual for correct hookup procedures.

ADDITIONAL SAFETY CONCERNS

LOADERS

Never tow a tractor by attaching a tow chain or cable to any part of the loader. Towing by the loader can cause a rollover.

When the loader is not needed, remove it from the tractor. Keeping it on the tractor limits visibility, impairs handling, and increases fuel consumption. Make sure stored loaders are properly blocked in a stable position. This will not only make them easier to hook up; it lessens the chance of a crushing injury.

This Could Be You...Donna had yelled for Gary, but he did not answer. How long was she supposed to wait in the skid steer with this pallet load of containers 10 feet up in the air? The plan was for Gary to be waiting at the second floor with the loading door open. She then could drop off the pallet and be on her way. What was taking him so long? Donna decided she'd speed things up. She'd just hop out and open the door herself. She was half way out when her foot bumped the steering lever. The skid steer suddenly lunged to the left knocking Donna off balance. She had just started to sense the sharp pain in her leg when she heard the thuds of falling chemical jugs. Besides the sore leg she now had a chemical spill to deal with. Where was Gary?

BACKHOES

Never operate backhoe controls from the ground. You could get crushed. Be aware of the backhoe's pinch points. Never let anyone in or near the swing pivot area (Fig. 11). If someone comes near, lower the bucket to the ground and shut off the engine.

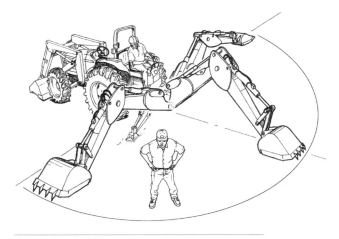

Fig. 11 – Keep Swing Pivot Area Clear of All Helpers

Properly stabilize the tractor before you start digging. Lower stabilizers until they firmly support and level the tractor (Fig. 12), then lower the front loader to provide additional stability. Make sure parking brake is engaged.

Never dig under the machine or its stabilizers. A cave-in could result and the machine could fall into the excavation.

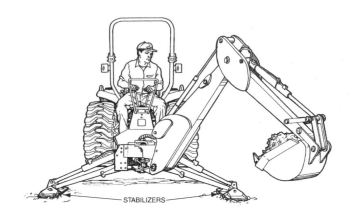

Fig. 12 – Machine Stabilizers

When operating on a slope, swing the backhoe to the uphill side to dump the load. That way if there is a stability problem while unloading, you won't roll down the hill. Downhill dumping can affect stability. If you must downhill dump, use extreme caution.

SKID STEERS

Most skid-steer loaders have a safety interlock or operator presence system. It may require the operator to be in the seat with the seat belt fastened before the engine can be started or lift arms and bucket operated. If the safety interlock system on your skid steer is not working, get it repaired at once. Never bypass the system. It is there for your protection.

Since skid-steer loaders are designed for compactness and maneuverability, the operator is very close to the lift arms and bucket. The operator also gets on and off the machine by stepping over the lift arms, and around or very near the controls. For your safety, the engine must be off before you exit or enter (Fig. 13). If not, bumping a control could cause the machine, or loader arms, to move.

Keep the operator's cab free of dirt, chains, or other objects. Skid steers have a rather confined space for the operator. Extra stuff in the operator area will interfere with safe operation of control levers and pedals. They could also cause you to fall or trip during exit and entry.

Fig. 13 – Enter and Exit Only with the Engine Shut Off and the Lift Arm and Attachments Lowered

Never enter the cab or reach into it unless lift arms are lowered and attachments are flat on the ground. Raised lift arms and bucket can fall causing serious injuries.

Before start-up, clear others from the area. Adults and children can be blocked from your view and run over. Check all around the machine to make sure that no one is nearby.

SEAT BELT

Always wear your seat belt. The loader can move suddenly and violently on rough terrain or in quick stops. Without a seat belt, you can be pitched against the inside of the machine or tossed out and run over. Stay alert for holes, rocks, rough surfaces, or other terrain hazards.

Keep your entire body inside the operator's station. Never reach or lean outside the cab. The lift arms or bucket could crush you as they move up or down or unexpectedly fall. Keep all protective screens or guards in place to prevent such serious injuries.

Fig. 14 – Keep the Bucket Low while Driving

The bucket should be kept low whenever you are driving (Fig. 14), especially if the bucket is loaded. That keeps the machine's center of gravity low and lessens the chance of a rollover. Raising the bucket moves the center of gravity upward and forward. Bumps, holes, rocks, and loose fill can easily upset a loader if the bucket is carried high.

Since skid steers are compact enough to work inside some buildings, exhaust gasses are a special concern. If you work indoors, make sure there is an adequate flow of fresh air. Exhaust gasses contain **carbon monoxide**, a deadly gas that's odorless and invisible. It can kill without warning. If the work area is a closed space, add fresh air by opening doors or windows, or by running exhaust fans.

Before unbuckling the seat belt and leaving the seat, lower the lift arms and attachment completely to the ground. Then put controls in PARK, set the parking brake, stop the engine, and remove the key. Cycle the hydraulic controls to relieve pressure.

ADDITIONAL RESOURCES

Backhoe Loader—Safety Manual, Equipment Manufacturers Institute, Chicago IL

Skid Steer Loader—Safety Manual, Equipment Manufacturers Institute, Chicago IL

There's lots of safety-related information and links at the National Ag Safety Database:
www.cdc.gov/niosh/nasd/nasdhome.html

"Safe Operation of John Deere Skid Steers" is a free video tape available from your local John Deere dealer.
Ask for part# DSVHC018312.

TEST YOURSELF

QUESTIONS - CHAPTER 6

1. What happens to a tractor's center of gravity when you raise a loader bucket?

2. Name three important safety concerns with loaders.

3. Why should a loader be lowered to the ground before you get out of the seat?

4. How can load rollback cause injuries?

COMMON ATTACHMENTS FOR COMPACT TRACTORS

Fig. 1 – Attachments Help Compact Tractors Perform Many Duties

INTRODUCTION

Compact tractors are versatile machines that can do many jobs. Much of this versatility comes from the attachments available for these tractors (Fig. 1). In this chapter we'll discuss safety issues concerning five popular attachments—front blades, rear blades, rotary-tine tillers, posthole diggers and front brooms.

(Front-end loaders and backhoe attachments are covered in Chapter 6, while rotary cutters are discussed in Chapter 8.)

SAFETY RESOURCES

All these attachments share two important safety features— an **operator's manual** and **safety warning signs**.

Never operate an attachment until you have read the operator's manual. Pay special attention to the safety information. If you can't find the operator's manual, contact your equipment dealer or the manufacturer for a new copy.

⚠ **WARNING**

TO HELP AVOID INJURY FROM PTO:

• Keep all shields in place.
• Keep hands, feet and clothing away.
• Operate only with 540 rpm.

Fig. 2 – Safety Signs Alert you to Potential Hazards on the Machine

Safety warning signs are found right on the equipment (Fig. 2). They alert you to potential safety hazards. Read each sign to understand the potential hazard, and then follow the sign's advice. Always heed these warnings. If safety-warning signs are damaged or worn off, see your equipment dealer for a new set.

HAZARDS IN COMMON

Hitching mishaps are a potential hazard common to all attachments. That's why it's important to take special care when attaching, detaching, and storing any attachment.

Here's the best way to hook up an attachment.

1. Have the attachment properly stored or blocked. This makes it easy to line up the attaching points on the tractor with those on the attachment.

2. Back the tractor up to the attachment, lining up the attaching points.

3. Shut off the tractor and lock the brakes (or shift into Park).

4. Get off and complete the attaching process.

Use tractor power to line up the attaching points. Never try to push or rock the attachment into place. This greatly increases the chance that the attachment will fall off its support and onto you.

Fig. 3 – Never Pull or Push an Attachment into Place

Likewise, don't push or pull the tractor to gain that last inch or two needed to line up attaching points. Once you get the tractor rolling it can be difficult to stop. It may only stop after it has pinned you between the tractor and the attachment.

It takes time to safely hook up an attachment. Don't takes chances or shortcut.

Fig. 4 – Never Let Anyone Between the Tractor and the Attachment while the Tractor is in Reverse

Helpers risk severe injury if they get between the tractor and the attachment while the tractor is in reverse (Fig. 4). If the driver's foot slips off the clutch, or a hand bumps a hydraulic lever, there's a good chance the helper will be injured

This Could Be You...hooking up the rear tiller was going to take longer than Carlos had intended. The parking stand had sunk into the mud leaving the tiller cock-eyed. Why the tiller had been parked outside, and not blocked up better, he didn't know. He called to Sylvia to give him a hand. Sylvia got in between the tiller and tractor as Carlos backed up close. The attaching points were off by just inches, so Sylvia started rocking the tiller to line things up. Suddenly Sylvia's footing slipped on the mud, bashing her head and shoulder against the tractor's 3-point hitch. But that wasn't the worst of it. As Carlos leaned back to see if Sylvia was hurt, he bumped the hitch control lever, causing the hitch to raise and crush Sylvia's hand against the tiller. Two hours later, as they both sat in the emergency room, the tiller still wasn't hooked up.

Protect Your Helper

While helpers may speed hooking up attachments, they also increase the chances of an injury. Never allow helpers to stand between the tractor and the implement while the tractor is backing up. Helpers should always stand to the side while the tractor is in reverse (Fig. 5). Only after the tractor is in park is it safe for a helper to go between the tractor and the implement to complete the hitching process.

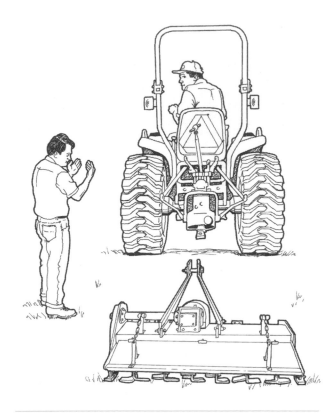

Fig. 5 – Helpers should Stand to the Side while the Tractor is in Reverse

FRONT AND REAR BLADES

Front and rear blades allow your tractor to clear snow, level gravel, and move dirt. Rear blades generally attach to the tractor's 3-point hitch and are raised and lowered by the hitch control lever (Fig. 6). A front blade, as you may have guessed, attaches to the front of the tractor. It is generally raised and lowered by using the tractor's **selective control valve**, or SCV (Fig. 7). Both front and rear blades may be equipped with a hydraulic cylinder to change the angle of the blade.

Fig. 6 – Rear Blades Attach to a Tractor's 3-point Hitch

Fig. 7 – Front Blades are Controlled by the Tractor's Selective Control Valve (SCV)

Common hazards involving front and rear blades include:

- **Crushing Incidents**
- **Collisions**
- **Hitching Mishaps (see beginning of chapter)**

CRUSHING INCIDENTS

Crushing incidents typically occur when the blade falls or is lowered onto feet or hands. On some tractors the blade will fall very rapidly when the control lever is lowered. It's easy for fingers or toes to be crushed before there is any time to react.

Keep hands and feet out from under the blade at all times (Fig. 8). If you must adjust or lubricate the blade, make sure it is in the lowest possible position, preferably with blade edge on the ground. Keep all people away from a blade until it is safely lowered to the ground, and the tractor is shut off.

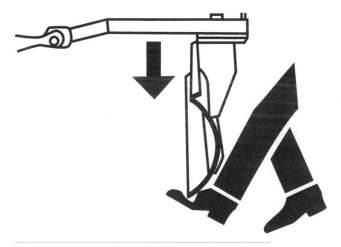

Fig. 8 — Keep Hands and Feet from Under the Blade

Make sure blades are properly supported during storage. This not only makes the blade easier to hook up; it also lessens the chance of crushed fingers and toes.

Crushing incidents can also happen when the blade angle changes. That's because many front or rear blades feature a hydraulic pivot control. Keep all bystanders and helpers away from the blade when the tractor is running (Fig. 9). Blades that pivot hydraulically can surprise and injure bystanders. An accidental bump of a hydraulic lever could cause the blade to pivot wildly.

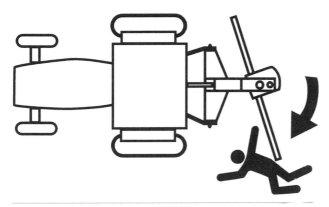

Fig. 9 – Never Allow People Near the Blade when the Tractor is Running

 CAUTION: Safety Alert: Most front blades feature a spring trip system. Make sure the blade is in the neutral position, and that all spring pressure has been released before checking the blade.

Fig. 10 – Most Front Blades Feature a Spring Trip System

COLLISIONS

Both rear and front blades change the effective length and width of your tractor (Fig. 11). This is especially true on turns. Use extra care when driving with a blade attached. Never drive between jobs with the blade in the tilted or offset position. This only adds to the change in dimensions, and the likelihood of a mishap. Pay attention when you drive near obstructions. Also be aware that a blade makes a large arc when you turn.

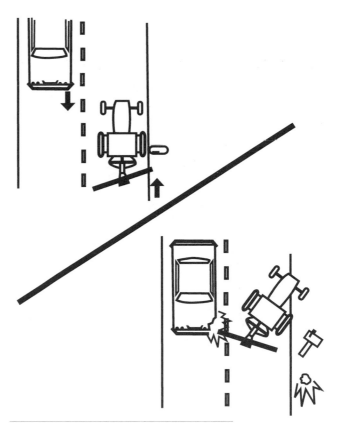

Fig. 11 – A Blade can make your Tractor Wider

Another cause of collisions is reduced ground clearance. If a blade is not fully raised, it can greatly lower your ground clearance (Fig. 12). To avoid hitting obstructions, raise blade up before you drive between jobs. During transport, keep the blade fully raised, drive slowly and always wear your seat belt.

Fig. 12 – A Blade can Greatly Change your Ground Clearance

ROTARY TINE TILLERS

To quickly work up soil, you can't beat a rotary tiller. The rotating blades cut through weeds and hard soil to give you a smooth, fine place to plant. Rotary-tine tillers make quick work of tilling the soil, but forget to follow safety rules, and these same rotating tines can be dangerous to life and limb.

Fig. 13 – Rotary Tine Tiller

Common mishaps involving rotary tillers include:

- **Entanglements**
- **Crushing incidents**
- **Hitching mishaps (see beginning of chapter)**

ENTANGLEMENTS

Getting entangled in a rotary tiller is extremely dangerous. At working speeds, rotary tiller tines turn at close to 200 rpms. That means the tine tip is moving about 14 feet per second. Any entanglement at those speeds would cause a serious injury.

Fig. 14 – Rotating Tines of a Tiller can Cause Severe Injury

That's why it's so important to follow proper safety procedures when working with a rotary tiller. Following these rules will prevent entanglements:

- **Never get off the tractor with the tiller running**
- **Keep other parties away while the tractor is running**
- **Never unplug a tiller with the tractor running**

Keep area clear of all bystanders, especially children and pets. Shut off the tractor if they come in the vicinity of your tiller

Unplugging a tiller is a special concern. It's not unusual for plant material to get wrapped up on the tiller tines. If this happens, stop the tiller and shut off the tractor before dismounting. Since material can get wound very tightly, you'll probably need a screwdriver or scraper to loosen up the plug. Wear gloves. The tine edges can be very sharp (Fig. 15).

If plugging happens often, you may need to cut or remove plant material on the ground you are tilling. By mowing the area first, you'll chop and shorten the plants, making wrapping and plugging much less likely.

Fig. 15 – Shut Off the Tractor and Wear Gloves when Working On or Near the Blades

CRUSHING INCIDENTS

Tillers are very heavy. Depending on working width, they can weigh anywhere between 300 and 700 pounds. A falling tiller could cause serious injury.

When you make adjustments or repairs, it's best to have the tiller attached to the tractor with the tiller lowered to the ground, or onto sturdy blocks.

When you store the tiller, make sure it is rock solid—on firm, level ground. This not only makes storage safer; it will also simplify attaching the tiller to the tractor the next time you need it.

OTHER SAFETY CONCERNS

Scout Before you Till
Make sure the area you are about to till is free of objects that could damage or plug your tiller. That means removing large rocks, branches, and cans or other trash.

Check for Underground Electrical Cables
What you can't see could also hurt you. Check for telephone, electrical and water lines before you till any new ground.

Check Ballast
A heavy tiller on the back of your tractor can affect tractor steering. Make sure you have enough ballast on the front of your tractor so the front wheels are always firmly on the ground.

Tillers can Affect Tractor Handling
If you are tilling too deep, or on very hard ground, the spinning tines may actually push your tractor ahead. Be prepared to shut off the PTO if you start to lose control of the tractor.

Till Safely on Slopes
If you are tilling on a slope, the tiller may actually act as sort of an anchor, slowing you down. Lifting the tiller out of the ground may cause the tractor to suddenly accelerate. Always drive slowly on slopes and be prepared to apply the brakes. Use special caution when tilling on slopes. The tractor may surge forward when you raise or lower the tiller.

Fig. 16 – Use Special Caution when Tilling on Slopes

POSTHOLE DIGGERS

A posthole digger is a tractor-driven auger that can drill holes in the ground. This tool is a great help when installing posts, fences, or planting trees. While posthole diggers make quick work of digging holes they have also removed many hands and arms from careless operators. Safe operation requires that you understand the potential hazards, and follow safety rules.

Fig. 17 — Posthole Digger

Common hazards involving posthole diggers include:

- **Entanglements**
- **Hitching mishaps (see beginning of chapter)**

ENTANGLEMENTS

A posthole digger is a great tool, but to do its job the auger needs to spin unshielded. Unless proper precautions are taken, the operator, or a bystander, could easily get entangled. Here's how to prevent those entanglements.

Keep Everyone Clear of the Digger and Powershafts when the Auger is Turning
Stop the auger when you are not digging. Keep all shields in place.

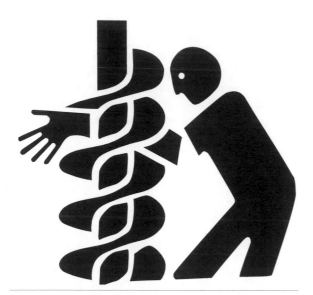

Fig. 18 – Keep Everyone Away from Auger while it is Turning

Wear Proper Clothing

That means a close-fitting shirt, pants and jacket. Never wear jewelry, scarves, or clothing with drawstrings. These all can get entangled in the rotating auger and shafts. Keep long hair securely tied up above the shoulders.

Use Correct Shear Pins

Most posthole diggers are protected by a shear pin that will break when there's too much force placed on the drives. Be sure to use the right shear pin for your digger. Shear pins or other bolts that are too long make it easier for the posthole digger to entangle clothes or hair. Never use shear pins longer than necessary. Pins that are too long can more easily catch clothing and cause serious injury.

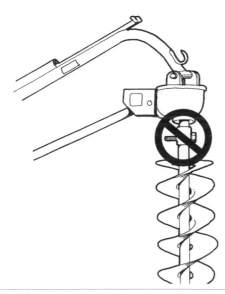

Fig. 19 – Use Only the Correct Bolts and Shear Pins. Bolts that are Too Long can Cause Warping.

Use Care Backing Out a Stuck Auger

Sometimes an auger gets stuck on wet clay, stones, or tree roots. Immediately disengage the PTO and turn off the engine. Then turn the auger backwards with a large wrench. Remove the wrench and then attempt to raise the auger hydraulically (Fig. 20). While the wrench is attached, the tractor must be turned off. If the PTO accidentally started, or the auger suddenly raised, the wrench could cause serious injuries.

Fig. 20 – Use Care Backing Out a Stuck Auger

This Could Be You…there were just two more holes to dig when Dave and Pat encountered the big rock. Using a crow bar they had managed to break the rock into several pieces, but the posthole digger refused to go any deeper. Dave had an idea. They just needed to get a little more weight on the auger so it could catch the rock pieces and pull them to the surface. So he tied one end of a rope onto the posthole digger's gearbox, and wrapped the other end around his hand for a good grip. He would pull down on the rope as the auger turned and that would do it. It looked like it was going to work, at least for the first 15 seconds. Pat never did figure out how the auger caught the rope. One instant Dave was pulling on the rope, the next instant the rope, and Dave, were wrapped around the auger.

OTHER SAFETY CONCERNS

Dig Each Hole in Small Steps
Dig down several inches, and then bring the auger up to let the soil clear. Repeat this procedure until the desired depth is reached. Run the auger as slowly as possible. You'll have better control and do a better job.

Keep Auger on the Ground when Not in Use
The auger can drop rapidly when the hitch lever is moved. When not in use, make sure tractor PTO is shut off and the auger is safely dropped to the ground.

Check Transport Clearance
When transporting a posthole digger, keep the posthole digger fully raised and watch for obstructions that could hit the auger.

Check Tractor Ballast
While posthole diggers are not extremely heavy, their weight is extended out the rear of the tractor. This leverage makes proper ballasting very important (Fig.22). Check your operator's manual to be sure you have correct weight on the front of your tractor.

PINHOLE HYDRAULIC LEAKS

Hydraulic fluid, coming from pinhole leaks, is under high-pressure and can easily penetrate human skin, flesh, and eyes and cause serious health risks. If any fluid is injected into the skin, a doctor familiar with this type injury must surgically remove it within a few hours. If the injury isn't treated gangrene may result.

Fig. 21 – Beware of Hydraulic Leaks

To make matters worse, these pinhole leaks can be very hard to detect. You may see only the symptoms of pinhole leaks. There may appear to be only dripping of fluid, when actually those drops are the accumulation of fluid from a high-pressure spray so fine it is invisible.

FRONT WEIGHTS

Fig. 22 – Be Sure Tractor is Properly Ballasted

Never try to locate a leak by touching a wet hose with a bare or even a gloved hand. Instead, wear safety glasses and pass a piece of cardboard or wood over the suspected area. Relieve pressure before correcting the leak.

ROTARY BROOMS

Rotary brooms use a cylinder-shaped brush, spinning at a high speed, to quickly clean and sweep large areas. They can be used to clear areas of dirt, leaves, and snow. The brooms usually attach to the front of a tractor (Fig. 23).

Fig. 23 – Front Brooms Turn your Compact Tractor into a Master Sweeper

Common hazards involving rotary brooms include:

- **Thrown objects**
- **Entanglements**
- **Hitching mishaps (see beginning of chapter)**

THROWN OBJECTS

A rotary broom typically spins at 200 rpms. That means the bristle tips are moving about 15 feet per second. That also means swept material shoots out the front of the broom at a similar speed (Fig. 24). If you are just sweeping leaves, or grass clippings, that's not a big deal. But if your broom hits stones, sticks, or glass, someone could easily get injured.

Fig. 25 – Thrown Material can Ricochet and Injure the Operator

Bystanders aren't the only ones in danger of thrown material. Even though swept material is directed forward, stones and other hard objects can ricochet back at the driver (Fig. 25). Always wear safety glasses when operating a rotary broom.

ENTANGLEMENTS

Rotary brooms have two components that can cause entanglements—the driveline and the brush. The best way to avoid any entanglement is to keep everyone away from rotating parts (Fig. 26). Never go near a drive unless the tractor is shut off, never leave the tractor seat with the PTO running, and never let a helper or bystander near the broom while the tractor is running.

Fig. 24 – Objects Thrown by a Rotating Broom can Reach Speeds of 15 Feet per Second

Preventing these injuries starts before you ever start sweeping.

Scout the Area you are to Sweep
Pick up cans, stones, and other objects that could cause damage if thrown. Stop the broom before you cross a gravel road or path.

Even after you have scouted the area, always direct the swept material away from people. If people or pets enter the work area, stop the broom until everyone has left.

Fig. 26 – Keep Hands, Feet and Clothing away of Rotating Broom

OTHER CONCERNS

Hydraulic Leaks

Brooms generally use hydraulic power to raise and angle the broom. Make sure hydraulic hoses do not touch or rub against tractor or broom frame. Rubbing can cause hoses to wear. Repair leaky hoses or connections as soon as you discover them.

Crushing Mishaps

If your rotary broom features hydraulic angling and hydraulic lift, there is the chance a person could get crushed between the broom and the tractor (Fig. 28). Never allow people near the broom while the tractor is running. Even with the PTO shut off, an accidental bump of the hydraulic lever could cause an injury. Make all broom adjustments with the tractor shut off and the broom lowered to the ground.

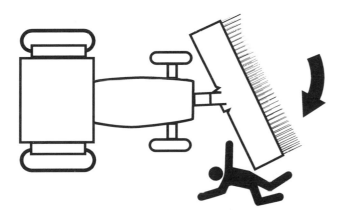

Fig. 28 – The Hydraulic Pivot could Crush Someone Between the Broom and the Tractor

ADDITIONAL RESOURCES

Check out the National Ag Safety Database:
www.cdc.gov/niosh/nasd/nasdhome.html

TEST YOURSELF

QUESTIONS - CHAPTER 7

1. Name two important considerations when storing an attachment.

2. When hooking up an attachment, why should a helper never stand behind the tractor when it is in reverse?

3. What must you do before attempting to unplug a rotary tiller?

4. What should you do if a posthole digger gets stuck in the ground?

5. Why are rotating brooms a special concern to second parties?

ROTARY MOWERS AND CUTTERS

INTRODUCTION

Rotary cutters and mowers do their cutting with a horizontal blade rotating at a very high speed. The most common machine that uses this design is the family lawn mower.

Underneath the typical small lawn mower, you'll find one blade that spins at a high speed (Fig. 1). Large, commercial-sized mowers may have two or more blades.

Lawn mowers and other rotary mowers are designed for light-duty mowing of lawns, parks, and ball fields. These machines come in a variety of shapes and sizes – from walk-behind models (Fig. 2) to riding lawn mowers to commercial front-mount mowers (Fig. 3) to compact tractors with mid-mount mower attachment (Fig. 4).

Fig. 1 – Blade underneath Small Lawn Mower

Fig. 2 – Commercial Walk-Behind Mower

Fig. 3 – Commercial Front-Mount Mower

Fig. 4 – Compact Tractor with Mid-Mount Mower Attachment

Rotary cutters (Fig. 5) use the same cutting concept to do more heavy-duty mowing. They are typically mounted on the tractor's 3-point hitch and are used to mow roadsides, pastures, or weed- or bush-covered fields. Some heavy-duty models can mow down small trees, 3 inches or more in diameter.

Fig. 5– Rotary Cutter

While these mowing machines may look quite different, they share many of the same safety concerns.

THE HARSH STATISTICS

These safety concerns translate into a huge number of injuries. According to the National Safety Council, lawnmower mishaps in the United States result in close to 75,000 emergency room visits each year.

Most of these mowing injuries fall under three categories:

- **Injuries caused by contacting the blade.**
- **Injuries caused by flying objects thrown by the blade.**
- **Injuries caused by losing control of the mower.**

Most, if not all, of these injuries could have been avoided if operators had followed the safety advice in their operator manuals, and on safety warning labels on the machines.

Let's look at how to prevent injuries in these three important areas.

PREVENTING BLADE INJURIES

A typical lawn mower blade spins at 3,000 revolutions per minute (rpms). That means a blade edge passes any one spot about 100 times per second. If you come in contact with a spinning blade, you are going to get seriously injured (Fig. 6).

Fig. 6 – Contact with Spinning Blade will cause Serious Injury

The obvious way to prevent blade injuries is to keep hands and feet away from a moving blade. But in the rush to get a mowing job done, thousands of these mishaps happen, caused by poor working conditions, poorly adjusted machines and careless operators.

SAFETY BEFORE YOU MOW

Safety starts before you start the engine. Check that all safety features are intact. Guards, shields, deflectors, and warning signs are on the machine to protect you and others. If any safety features have been damaged or altered, do not use the mower until they are fixed. Make sure the mowing area is clear of all obstacles.

Safety seat switch stops the mower blades if you forget to turn them off before leaving the seat.

Interlock system assures engine will not start unless mower blades are turned off and traction drive is disengaged.

Discharge chute helps protect you from flying debris.

Easy-to-read safety labels warn you of mowing dangers.

Fig. 7 – Safety Features found on many Lawn Tractors

Be sure all safety interlock systems are working. Typically these systems will shut off the engine or stop the blade from turning if the operator leaves the seat, or lets go of the handle. These systems are also sometimes called operator-presence systems because they show the operator is present in a safe operating position. Never bypass or disable these systems. They are there to protect all operators.

The handles on a typical operator-presence system on a walk-behind mower must be squeezed together for the mower to work (Fig. 8). Never operate a mower if this safety system has been disconnected or bypassed.

Squeeze Handles Together

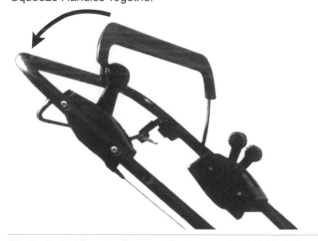

Fig. 8 – Typical Operator-Presence System on a Walk-Behind Mower

Before you undertake any service on a mower, make sure the engine is shut off and cannot be started. Turn off the key and remove it. If the machine doesn't have a key, pull off the spark plug wire. This will ensure the engine cannot start while service is being performed.

On PTO-driven mowers and rotary cutters, never leave the tractor unless the PTO and the tractor engine are shut off. Having both turned off limits the chance that a helper will accidentally engage the PTO.

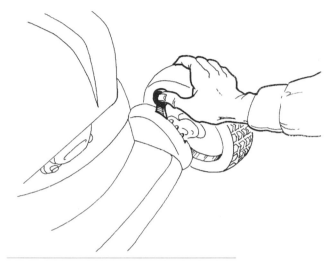

Fig. 9 – Adjusting Lever on Walk-Behind Mower

Cutting height on some walk-behind mowers is set by individually adjusting wheel height (Fig. 9). Never do this with the engine running. These adjustments bring your hand close to the mower blade.

Having the mower in tiptop condition will eliminate many problems. Blades should be kept sharp. Sharp blades make cutting easier and leave more engine power to discharge cut material. Any blade that is cracked, bent, or out of balance should be discarded immediately.

Also make sure the discharge area is clean and the discharge deflector properly positioned. This will aid the flow of grass and material out of the mower.

Fig. 10 – Underside of Mower deck

SAFETY WHILE YOU ARE MOWING

Many injuries happen when the operator tries to clear a plugged mower. Keep fingers and toes away from the blade areas when the engine is running. Always assume the blade is turning when the engine is running. There is very little clearance between the blade tip and the inside surface of the mower deck (Fig. 10). Never attempt to remove debris near the mower deck with the engine running.

Also, never clean the discharge area when the engine is running. Turn off the engine and be sure the blade has stopped before making any corrections. Use a stick or tool to unplug the discharge area. Even a stopped blade is sharp and could hurt you.

Poor operating conditions also increase the chances of plugging. Avoid mowing grass when it is wet. Wet grass generally does not bag or discharge properly. Also don't expect a light-duty mower to do heavy-duty mowing. A mower designed for mowing lawns will not perform well cutting brush or knee-high grass. The mower will likely plug, and frustrate the operator. And frustrated operators take more chances and cause more mishaps.

PREVENTING THROWN-OBJECT INJURIES

We noted earlier that the typical lawn mower blade spins at 3,000 revolutions per minute. That means the speed of the blade tip can approach 200 miles per hour. Plus many blades are shaped to create a vacuuming action to stand the grass up for a cleaner cut. Because of this, the blade can pick up debris like small rocks, broken glass or sticks and throw them out the discharge chute with considerable force. A harmless-looking stick can become dozens of speeding "bullets" (Fig. 11). Before you mow, check the lawn for objects that could be thrown.

Fig. 11 – A Lawn Mower can turn a Stick into Dozens of Speeding "Bullets"

When mowing a lawn, you can prevent most thrown objects by walking the area and picking up things your lawn mower might throw. Rocks, sticks, toys, cans, bottles, etc., should all be removed before you start the lawn mower.

Wherever you are mowing – lawn, field, or roadside – keep the area is clear of pets, children, and bystanders. (When mowing around a home, keep children and pets safely in the house.) If anyone enters the mowing area, shut off the mower until he or she leaves.

Your mower's discharge deflector is designed to direct thrown objects downward toward the grass (Fig. 12). Raising, removing, or repositioning the deflector will greatly increase the chances of a thrown-object injury and also greatly increase the distance a thrown object can fly. Keep all shields and deflectors in place and properly adjusted.

Fig. 12 – The Discharge Chute Deflects Thrown Objects Downward

Never go across driveways or paths with the blade running. The blade can pick up and throw gravel stones and loose rocks.

Protect your feet and legs from thrown objects. Wear closed-toe, heavy-duty shoes with good traction soles – not tennis shoes or sandals. Also wear sturdy, long pants – sorry, no shorts.

This Could Be You...Les was just about done mowing the lawn, and good thing too – it was getting dark and the grass was becoming damp. Five times in the past five minutes he'd had to clear a plug from the discharge chute. He had only that little hill to mow under the poplar tree. He hated mowing that hill – mainly because it was such a pain to push that mower up the hill. But last time he mowed he tried pulling the mower backward up the hill and that worked much better. And it was working tonight as well, at least until his left foot slipped. Les wasn't sure what caused him to slip – the damp grass, a small stick from that poplar tree? What Les does remember happened in slow motion. He remembers his left foot going under the mower, him letting go of the mower and seeing it roll down the hill, And then looking at his foot, his white tennis shoe quickly turning red.

PREVENTING LOSS-OF-CONTROL INJURIES

As with any piece of outdoor power equipment, you can't be a safe operator unless you are fully in control. Get familiar with the controls and how the machine handles before you start the engine.

If you are new to the machine or the job, drive around the area to be mowed with the blade shut off (Fig. 13). This will let you get the feel of the machine before you start mowing.

Fig. 13 — Practice Mowing with Blade Shut-off to get a feel of how the Mower Operates

R o t a r y   M o w e r s   a n d   C u t t e r s

With a little experience, control will not be a problem, especially if the ground is flat and dry. But control can become a serious issue for anyone who mows on slopes or mows damp grass.

Let's look at the different control issues with walk-behind mowers and riding or tractor-driven mowers and cutters.

CONTROL OF WALK-BEHIND MOWERS

Controlling a walk-behind mower starts with your feet. You can't have good control unless you have good traction. Wear sturdy work boots with aggressive soles. You'll need them to keep a good grip on the turf.

That good grip becomes extra important if the grass is wet or damp. Wet grass limits your footing, making it easier for a foot to slide into the blade path. Wet or damp grass is also more likely to plug the discharge area. If you must mow in wet or very humid conditions, use extreme caution. If your footing is poor, or it's difficult to control the mower, wait for the turf to dry.

Fig. 14 – Operate Across the Slope when using a Walk-Behind Mower

Mow across slopes with walk-behind mowers (Fig. 14). If it's difficult to control the mower, do not mow the slope. Shut down the blade and move slowly down the slope. Slopes that are too steep to mow safely should be planted in ground covers or wild flowers.

Walk-behind mowers are designed to mow going forward. Mowing in reverse increases the chance of pulling the mower onto your foot. Whenever possible, mow going forward. If you must pull the mower in reverse, make sure you use extra care and have good footing.

CONTROL OF TRACTORS AND RIDING MOWERS

Slopes and wet grass are also a safety concern if you are riding. (For a general discussion of tractor rollovers, review the section about "Tractor Upsets" in Chapter 5).

The first step is to prepare your machine for slopes.

Make sure your tractor is properly **ballasted** to maintain steering. For 3-point hitch mowers, front weights may be needed on the tractor. For front-mount mowers, rear weight may be needed.

Fig. 15 – Extra Ballast may be needed to Maintain Good Steering Control

Set tractor tires as wide as possible. If you are operating a rotary cutter, try to set the rear tractor tires wider than the cutter frame. This not only provides greater tractor stability, it also increases your mowing efficiency since you'll not flatten some of the material about to be cut.

When mowing with a tractor or riding mower, mow up and down slopes (Fig. 16). This will increase your control. Mowing across slopes greatly increases the chance of rollover. When mowing on a slope, slow down. Use special care when changing directions. Keep the tractor or drive unit in gear at all times so the engine can act as a brake. Never coast down a hill.

Fig. 16 – Drive Up and Down the Slope when Operating a Riding Mower

Take extreme care when mowing wet grass. If tires start to spin or slide on the grass shut off the blade and slowly get off the slope. Wait for the grass to dry before attempting to mow.

Do not mow close to ditches, embankments, or other drop-offs (Fig. 17). The slightest mistake could cause you to lose control, resulting in a serious injury.

Fig. 17 – Do Not Mow Near Edge of Drop-off, Embankment or Gully

LANDSCAPE FOR SAFETY

Landscaping with safety in mind can make a lawn much easier and safer to mow and care for. Here are a few suggestions:

Round Out Corners
Mowing corners generally requires sharp turns and backing. By planting flowers or ground cover in corners, you'll find mowing faster and less frustrating.

Fill in Depressions and Low Spots
Holes are not only unattractive; they can cause a sprained ankle or a rougher ride. Get a bag of topsoil and some lawn seed and fix those holes and depressions.

Remove a Circle of Grass around Trees
Size the circle to a convenient turning radius of your lawn mower. Fill in the circle with shredded tree bark or other soft mulch. This will make trimming around trees easier, plus it will protect the tree from mower damage.

Remove Low-Hanging Tree Branches
Low branches not only make it inconvenient to mow around trees; they can be a safety hazard. They can knock off your glasses, limit your view of the lawn, and even knock you off balance. Removing those pesky branches makes mowing more pleasant and allows more light to reach the grass.

Don't Mow Steep Slopes
Take a careful look at any hillsides you mow. Planting that slope in ground cover or wild flowers could make mowing safer and more pleasant.

Fig. 18 – Mulched Areas can Speed Mowing, Limit Trimming, and Protect Trees and Shrubs from Mower Damage

OTHER SAFETY CONCERNS

Giving Children Rides
Never carry children in your lap on a riding mower. This reduces your ability to control the mower and diverts your attention from the mowing job. Giving rides, even with the blade shut off, is a bad idea. Children who are used to getting rides will approach a working lawn mower unaware of the danger. Don't tempt fate. Never give rides!

Sudden Strange Noises or Vibrations
If a blade hits an obstruction and is bent or damaged, the mower or cutter may suddenly vibrate or make strange noises. Immediately shut down the mower, turn off the engine, and check for damage. Never operate a machine with a cracked, bent or out-of-balance blade.

Carbon Monoxide
Mower engines all give off carbon monoxide, a deadly odorless and colorless gas. Never run an engine in a closed space, even for a short time.

Refueling
Always shut off the engine before refueling. If the engine is hot let it cool for several minutes before adding fuel. Always refuel outdoors. Dangerous fumes can collect indoors. Don't refuel with mower parked on the lawn, as spills can kill grass. Wipe up any spilled fuel before restarting the engine. And remember – no smoking!

This Could Be You...When William visited Grandpa's house; there was one sound he really loved to hear. It was the sound of Grandpa's lawn tractor starting up. That could mean just one thing, a tractor ride! Grandpa would put William on his lap and drive around the yard as long as William wanted. This was great. And then the day came when Grandpa was in the backyard, cutting his grass, when William and his parents arrived. Hearing the sound of the mower, William bolted out of the car and raced to the backyard. Grandpa never saw William come running around the corner of the house, never saw him running toward the lawn tractor, and never saw him trip and slide, hands first across the lawn. The only thing Grandpa saw was those little fingers disappearing under the mower deck.

Unattended Mowers
Before leaving a mower unattended, turn off the PTO or mower drives, shut off the engine, and remove the key. If it doesn't have a key, remove the spark-plug wire so a child or bystander can't start the mower. Lower 3-point hitch cutters and hydraulically controlled mower decks to the ground.

ADDITIONAL RESOURCES

Agricultural Tractor Safety Manual, Equipment Manufacturers Institute, Chicago, IL

How to Mow a Great Looking Lawn Safely, American Honda Motor Co., Duluth, GA

Mowing Safety Know-How, Deere & Company, Moline, IL

Think and Live Safely, The Toro Company, Bloomington, MN

Search the National Ag Safety Database: www.cdc.gov/niosh/nasd/nasdhome.html

TEST YOURSELF

QUESTIONS - CHAPTER 8

1. List the three major causes of mower and rotary cutter injuries.

2. Why is it important to keep the discharge chute in the correct working position?

3. What is the recommended clothing for operating a walk-behind mower?

4. With a walk-behind mower, what is the correct direction to mow a hillside? How about with a riding mower?

5. List three ways landscaping can make a lawn safer to mow.

LAWN-GROOMING EQUIPMENT

9

INTRODUCTION

Once upon a time there was basically one power tool available to help you get a great-looking yard—a lawn mower. Other trimming and grooming tasks were accomplished by a variety of hand-powered tools—shears, rakes, an old kitchen knife.

Today that trimming job has been made much easier and quicker thanks to a host of outdoor power equipment—line trimmers, blowers, hedge trimmers, and the like. Line trimmers can clean up those areas lawn mowers can't easily reach (Fig. 1); hedge trimmers keep shrubbery looking neat (Fig. 2); edgers give a crisp, finished look to a yard (Fig. 3); and backpack blowers can whisk away leaves and grass clippings (Fig. 4). While the power of these tools helps you accomplish more, they also increase the chance of injury if you don't follow proper safety precautions.

Fig. 1 – Line Trimmer

Fig. 2 – Hedge Trimmer

Fig. 3 – Edger

Fig. 4 – Backpack Blower

IMPORTANT SAFETY CONCERNS

There are many different lawn- and yard-grooming power tools available. And while these tools look different and can do different tasks, the types of mishaps they are involved in are quite similar. The majority of the injuries result from:

- **Poor operator protection**
- **Thrown objects**
- **Contact with moving parts.**

Let's look at each of these areas to better understand how to prevent lawn- and yard-grooming injuries.

OPERATOR PROTECTION

For many machines, injuries happen when safe operating procedures are not followed. But with these lawn- and yard-grooming tools, it's not enough to operate the machine safely; you also need to wear the recommended clothing and safety gear. Proper protective gear is important because the operator is so close to the moving parts (Fig. 5).

Fig. 5 – Operator is Close to Machine's Moving Parts

For example, line trimmers use a rapidly spinning string to cut grass and weeds. An operator who wears shorts and sandals takes a big chance that flying debris will not cause an injury. Likewise, leaf blowers can generate a lot of noise. If you follow all the safe-operating procedures but fail to wear hearing protection as recommended, you could damage your hearing.

To avoid these injuries, follow the clothing and safety gear recommendations in the machine's operator's manual. Often these recommendations will include:

- **Safety glasses**
- **Hearing protection**
- **Sturdy closed-toe shoes or work boots**
- **Long pants**
- **Long-sleeve shirt.**

Consider these recommendations to be the minimum requirement. Your working conditions may require additional protection. For example, if you are working in especially dusty conditions, you may want to wear a dust mask.

For further discussion of proper clothing, see the section on personal protective equipment in Chapter 2, Human Factors.

This Could Be You...the sun had come out from behind the clouds and suddenly Ryan was hot, very hot. He still had the edging to do and his safety glasses, which he had worn most of the morning, were getting fogged up. "Oh, why bother!" he thought, as he tossed the eye protection into the cab of the pickup. It wasn't three minutes later that Ryan knew "why bother." He had leaned over to check how close the spinning blade was to the sidewalk when a sharp pain suddenly ripped through his eye. It felt like stab from a hot knife. The doctor found not a knife, but a small chip of concrete.

THROWN OBJECTS

Many lawn-grooming tools use spinning parts—line trimmers and edgers, for example. These spinning components can throw objects, making them a hazard to both the operator and any bystander.

As we've just discussed, the operator should protect himself by wearing proper shoes, pants, and safety glasses. To protect others, you must keep them out of the **danger zone**.

The danger zone is the area around a power tool where thrown objects pose a serious hazard. For most line trimmers, edgers, and blowers, the danger zone extends in a 50-foot radius (15 meters or 16 paces) of the tool in all directions. Keep all helpers and bystanders out of the danger zone while the equipment is running. If any animal or person wanders into the danger zone, shut off the engine immediately. Don't restart until the zone is clear.

If a helper must be in the danger zone with operator, he or she must wear all the recommended personal protective equipment.

Even those outside the danger zone are at some risk to flying objects. Keep all bystanders well away when you operate any outdoor power tool.

Here are some other tips to reduce the chances of an injury from a thrown object.

Blowers
Use the slowest speed necessary to do the job. This not only reduces the danger of thrown objects; it also reduces the noise level. Blow material away from people and pets. Never point the blower pipe at anyone. Blowers can generate wind speeds approaching 200 miles per hour!

Fig. 7 – Blow Material Away from Co-workers and Bystanders

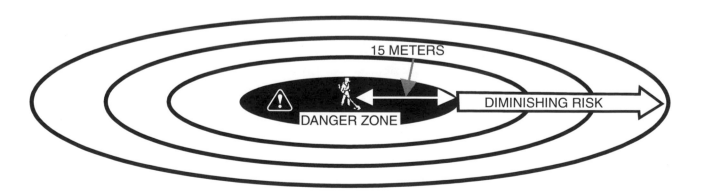

Fig. 6 – Danger Zone of Line Trimmer

Edgers

Scout the area to be edged, looking for stones, branches, and other debris that might get thrown. Do not use an edger on graveled surfaces. Keep all guards in place; they deflect thrown material downward and away from the operator (Fig. 8). Never operate an edger from any position other than what's recommended in the operator's manual.

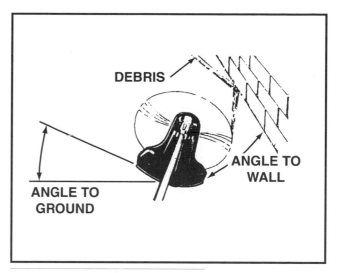

Fig. 9 – Trimming Near a Wall or a Fence

Keep trimmer low—near the ground. This tool is not made to trim shrubbery, climbing ivy, or other greenery above ground level.

Shields must be kept in place. The debris shield is especially important. It attaches just above the trimmer head and deflects cut material down, protecting the operator's legs.

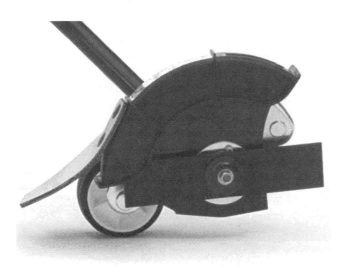

Fig. 8 – Keep All Edger Shields in Place

Line Trimmers

How you hold and operate a trimmer will affect the direction that cut material flies. By tilting the trimmer head slightly, you'll direct debris away from you.

Also take special concern when trimming near walls, fences, or other objects. Approach these barriers from an angle so that any debris that ricochets off the barrier will fly away from you (Fig. 9).

Fig. 10 – Grass/Weed Trimmer Shield

This Could Be You...Gloria had been trimming the overgrown hillside for 15 minutes and suddenly things weren't going well. The grass was longer here and it tended to wrap around the trimmer head. Finally the trimmer head stopped. It was plugged. Gloria reached down to pull at the twisted grass. She knew she should shut off the engine, but nothing was moving, and the engine was so hard to start when it was hot. She'd be careful. She grabbed the wad of grass and pulled. Suddenly it let go, causing Gloria to lose her balance, which caused her to bump the throttle, which caused the now-free trimmer head to start spinning. Unfortunately, now the trimmer head was resting against the bare skin that showed through her sandal. By the time she got back her balance and got control of the trimmer, her foot felt and looked like she had several hundred bee stings. A week later she was still walking with a limp.

CONTACT WITH MOVING PARTS

The best way to avoid injury from a moving part is to make sure the part is not moving. That may sound simple enough, but when you operate outdoor power equipment, and are in a hurry to complete a task, you may find yourself doing stupid things—such as clearing twigs off the blades of a hedge trimmer, or kicking a running line trimmer to knock grass off its head.

Remember, never do any service or make any adjustments while the engine is running. Before doing any cleaning, adjusting, or repair, shut off the engine and wait for all parts to come to a complete stop (Fig. 11).

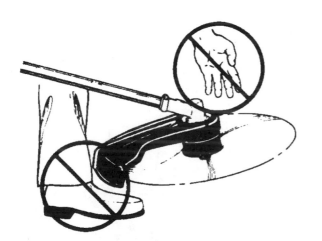

Fig. 11 – Keep Hands and Feet Away until Rotation has Stopped

It's not good enough to let the engine idle while you wait for moving parts to stop. On many lawn- and yard-grooming tools, accidentally bumping of the throttle will start parts moving again. Shut the engine off. It may take a little more effort, but it may also save a finger or toe.

Some injuries happen because the operator does not have good control of the machine. Wear sturdy shoes with traction soles. Firm footing is important for safe operation.

Keep both feet on the ground—no ladders; no step stools, and no overreaching. All are prescriptions for trouble.

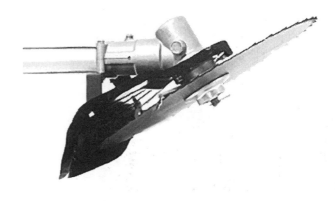

Fig. 12 – Line Trimmer Head with Brush Blade Installed

Watch for Kickout

Brushing-cutting blades can be installed on some heavy-duty line trimmers (Fig. 12). If the blade strikes a strong, solid object, the rotation of the blade may push the trimmer back violently. This is called **kickout**, and it's a serious risk to any helper or bystander near the trimmer (Fig. 13). The force of kickout could also throw the operator off balance.

Fig. 13 – Watch for Kickout

Make sure you have good footing and good control of the trimmer at all times. Keep all people and animals out of the danger zone when using a brush blade. A trimmer equipped with a brush blade may kickout if it contacts strong brush or trees. The direction of kickout will depend on the rotation of the brush-blade (Fig. 14).

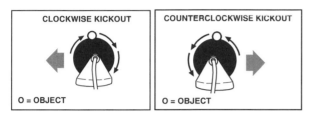

Fig. 14 – The Direction of Kickout Depends on the Rotation of the Brush-blade

OTHER CONCERNS

Refueling
Never refuel while an engine is running or hot. Move at least 10 feet from the fueling spot before starting the engine. Make sure there are no open flames, sparks or lit cigarettes when refueling.

Hot Surfaces
On many lawn- and yard-grooming machines hot engine parts are close to the operator. Be sure you know the location of the muffler and other hot surfaces and keep them away from skin and clothing.

Fig. 15 – Hot Surface Warning

Fire Prevention
Know your fire regulations. In some states and on some public land you must install spark arresters to outdoor power equipment. Make sure you are in compliance with local rules.

Electric Shock
House current and a long extension cord power some lawn and yard-grooming tools. Regularly inspect all cords, looking for cracks and signs of wear. Make sure these tools are plugged only into a circuit with **ground fault interrupt** protection (see chapter 16).

ADDITIONAL RESOURCES

Grass/Weed Trimmer, Brushcutter and Clearing Saw Safety Manual, Deere & Company, Moline IL

Safety Scope Safety Tips Handbook, Homelite, Charlotte NC

TEST YOURSELF

QUESTIONS - CHAPTER 9

1. What is a danger zone? How big is it for a typical line trimmer?

2. Why are safety glasses recommended when operating lawn-grooming equipment?

3. List the three major causes of injuries that can happen while operating lawn-grooming equipment.

SNOWBLOWING EQUIPMENT

INTRODUCTION

Snowblowers can be found either as a walk-behind machine, or as an attachment to the front or rear of compact tractors.

Fig. 1 – A Typical Walk-Behind Snowblower in Action

Most heavy-duty models feature a two-stage design. A horizontal converging auger (the first stage) breaks up the snow and feeds it into a center blower (the second stage). The blower throws the snow out a discharge chute. This chute can be rotated from side to side to direct the blown snow.

Fig. 2 – Snowblower Attachment for a Compact Tractor

IMPORTANT SAFETY CONCERNS

Entanglements are the number one cause of serious snowblower injuries. Every winter snowblowers move mountains of snow for careful operators. For those who aren't careful, they also remove far too many fingers and toes.

These injuries wouldn't happen if operators followed a simple safety rule:

Never attempt to dislodge stuck snow or debris from an operating snowblower. Shut off the engine and wait until all moving parts have stopped before going near the discharge chute or front auger. The discharge blower typically turns at close to 1,000 rpms. Fingers or a hand can be cut off in an instant.

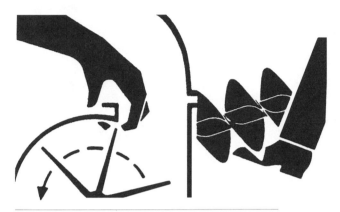

Fig. 3 – Keep Hands and Feet Away from Moving Parts

The rotating auger turns slower than the blower does, but it can pull your arm or foot into the machine causing severe injury. Even if you use a stick to poke at an obstruction, a moving auger can draw your hand in before you can react to let go.

Remember, always shut off the power and wait for all moving parts to stop before you attempt any work on or near the machine. Remove the key so others cannot accidentally start the snowblower. To do anything else risks serious injury.

This Could Be You...Phil couldn't believe it picked today to snow. There was a big breakfast meeting in the clubhouse, and he was the only one available to run the snowblower. To make matters worse, the heavy, wet snow did not blow well. Every few minutes the discharge chute would plug and he'd have to get off the tractor and clear the wet snow. He had just plugged the chute for the fifth time when Mary, who was shoveling some steps, came over to offer her assistance. Phil kept the machine running while Mary used her snow shovel to dislodge the plug of wet, sloppy snow. Suddenly Mary slipped. The shovel fell into the front auger. In an instant there was a shower of splintered wood and chunks of aluminum. Fortunately, no one was hurt, but it was a scare Phil and Mary will never forget.

OTHER CONCERNS

Refueling
Never refuel indoors. The gasoline spills and vapors are highly flammable. It may be cold outside, but that's where it's safest to refuel. If you run out of gas in the middle of a job let the engine cool down for a few minutes before refueling.

Carbon Monoxide
Even though some walk-behind snowblowers have small engines, they still put out deadly fumes. Never run a snowblower in a closed garage or shed. Get the machine outside where deadly carbon monoxide cannot build up.

Buried Objects
Check the area to be cleared for objects buried under the snow. Look for doormats, sleds, boards, wires, and other foreign objects. Raise the snowblower up when driving between jobs and drive slowly when removing snow.

Fig. 4 – Beware of Obstructions

Gravel Drives
Beware when clearing a gravel path. A snowblower can throw gravel and other objects in the snow with great force and at high speed, causing serious injury. Always direct blown snow away from people, pets, and windows. Use a shovel to remove snow that may contain large stones or other debris.

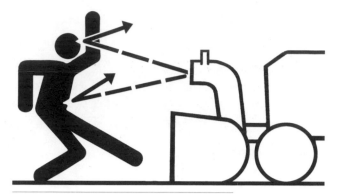
Fig. 5 – Use Special Care on Gravel Driveways

Hydraulic Leaks
Escaping fluid under pressure can penetrate the skin, causing a serious infection or reaction. Relieve pressure before disconnecting hydraulic lines. Be sure all connections are tight before applying pressure.

Ballast
Make sure your tractor is properly ballasted. Proper ballast assures good traction and control. Front- and rear-mounted snowblowers change the weight distribution on your tractor, affecting steering and braking. Check both tractor and snowblower operator manuals.

Fig. 6 – Ballast Box on the Rear of Tractor

ADDITIONAL RESOURCES
Think and Live Safely–Snowthrower Operator Safety Requirements, The Toro Co., Bloomington, MN

TEST YOURSELF

QUESTIONS - CHAPTER 10

1. Why should you never start a snowblower inside a building?

2. What must you always do before clearing a blocked discharge chute?

3. How does using a snowblower on a gravel driveway create a special hazard?

CHAIN SAWS AND LOG SPLITTERS

11

INTRODUCTION

In this chapter we will first discuss chain saws, and then look at safety issues concerning log splitters.

Chain saws are very useful tools. Compared to hand tools, they can make you more productive at pruning, removing trees and cleaning up after a storm. They are also safe tools IF used correctly by properly trained individuals wearing recommended personal protective equipment (PPE).

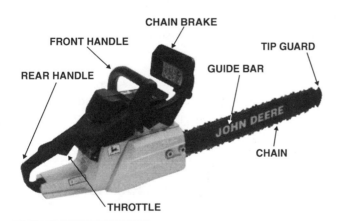

Fig. 1 – Part of a Chain Saw

But the fact of the matter is that poorly trained operators wearing no **PPE** often use chain saws incorrectly. This accounts for most of the 30,000 or so Americans who seek medical treatment each year as a result of chain saw injuries.

It's easy to see how misusing a chain saw could result in injuries. At full speed, the chain moves at close to 60 miles per hour. At that speed hundreds of cutting teeth pass a point each second. If a moving chain hits an unprotected operator, a serious injury will result.

Besides the fast-moving chain, operators also have to worry about falling tree branches and rolling logs. With all these hazards, it's no wonder so many people are injured by chain saws. In fact, after some major storms more people are injured using chain saws to clear fallen trees than are actually injured by the storms themselves.

KNOW YOUR LIMITS

Since a chain saw poses so many safety concerns, perhaps the first question you should ask is if you really need to use one. The Yellow Pages list many trained professionals who use a chain saw every day in their businesses. If there is serious storm damage, a large tree to fell, or pruning that requires a ladder, you are probably better off to hire the job done.

Also remember good old-fashioned hand tools. Pruning saws and shears may be slower, but they pose fewer hazards for the inexperienced chain-saw user.

IMPORTANT SAFETY CONCERNS

Most chain-saw mishaps can be divided into four broad categories:

- **Kickback**
- **Contact with the moving chain**
- **Loss of balance or control**
- **Falling material.**

KICKBACK

Let's talk first about one of the major causes of chain-saw injuries: kickback. To understand kickback you must first understand the reactive forces of a chain saw.

When a chain cuts its way into a log, the chain moves in one direction, which exerts a force onto the saw and the operator in the opposite direction (Fig. 2). Cut with the bottom of the guide bar, and the saw will pull away from you. Cut with the top of the guide bar and the saw will push back toward you. With a sharp chain, a proper stance, and a good grip on the chain saw, these reactive forces are generally easy to overcome.

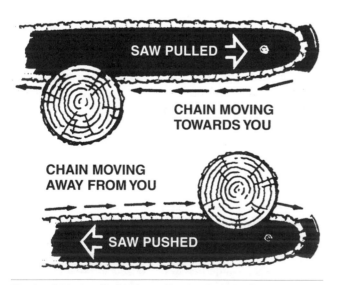

SAW PULLED

CHAIN MOVING TOWARDS YOU

CHAIN MOVING AWAY FROM YOU

SAW PUSHED

Fig. 2 – A Moving Chain Always Exerts a Reactive Force Onto the Chain Saw and the Operator

But when the tip of the guide bar contacts a log, the resulting reactive force is not so easy to control. This reactive force is called kickback because it causes the saw to kick back in an arc. Sometimes kickback happens with such speed and force that it sends the running saw right back at the operator. Serious or even fatal injuries can result.

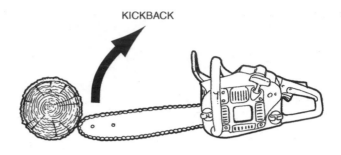

KICKBACK

Fig. 3 – Kickback

Kickback is the reactive force caused when the tip of the chain saw contacts a solid surface. It can cause the saw to rapidly pivot back toward the operator (Fig. 3).

A dangerous kickback does not happen every time the tip of the guide bar touches wood or some other solid surface, and that's part of the problem. An operator can cut for hours with never a hint of kickback. But if the tip of the saw strikes an embedded nail, or is pinched by a drooping branch, or bumps a second log on the far side of the cut, kickback can happen with such speed and force it is difficult to control. With the chain moving about 50 feet per second, the operator cannot react fast enough. Any operator who gets complacent about how he stands or how he holds the chain saw can get hurt in an instant.

Avoiding Kickback

To avoid kickback you need to have a properly maintained and outfitted saw and a proper operating stance. You also need to avoid certain cutting situations. Here are some tips:

1. **Make sure your saw has a chain brake.**
   A chain brake is a device that, if bumped, instantly stops the chain. With a chain brake, if the saw kicks back, your hand or arm will bump the brake, stopping the chain. While a chain brake does nothing to prevent kickback, it does stop the moving chain, greatly limiting the chance of serious injury.

HAND TRIPS BRAKE AND CHAIN IS STOPPED

Fig. 4 – Chain Brake

2. Never cut with the guide bar close to your body.

Even with a chain brake, depend on proper cutting methods and your good sense. For example, if the saw is held above mid-chest and kickback occurs, the chain brake may not have time to stop the chain before it hits you.

Fig. 5 – Never Cut with the Chain Saw Close to your Body

3. Hold the chain saw firmly.

Use both hands and maintain a secure grip. Stand to the side of the cutting path of the chain saw. This will position you out of the potential kickback path should kickback occur (Fig. 6).

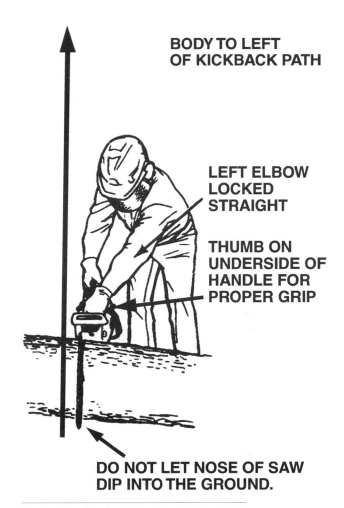

BODY TO LEFT OF KICKBACK PATH

LEFT ELBOW LOCKED STRAIGHT

THUMB ON UNDERSIDE OF HANDLE FOR PROPER GRIP

DO NOT LET NOSE OF SAW DIP INTO THE GROUND.

Fig. 6 – Stand to the Side of the Kickback Path

4. Watch your saw tip while you are cutting.

Make sure it doesn't strike any objects. Be especially careful when cutting small, tough limbs, small-sized brush, and samplings, which may easily catch the chain. Also be alert for the weight of a branch to close a cut, thus pinching the chain.

5. Cut only one log at a time.

If the tip of the guide bar contacts a second log, it can cause kickback.

6. Use extreme caution when re-entering a previous cut.

The tip of the guide bar can catch on the wood and cause kickback.

7. Attach a tip guard to the nose of your saw.

This covers the tip of the guide bar keeping material from touching it and is virtually 100 percent effective in preventing kickback (Fig. 8). The tip guard does, however, limit the ability of the saw to make some cuts and can make the saw more difficult to remove from a pinching log. In these cases, the tip guard can be removed.

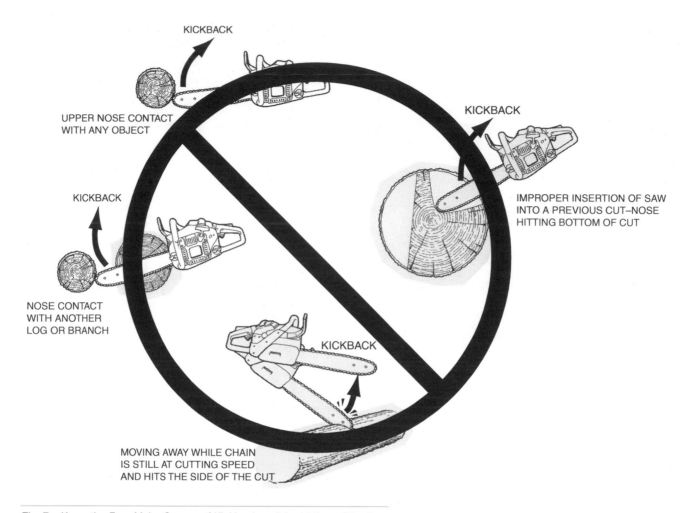

KICKBACK

UPPER NOSE CONTACT
WITH ANY OBJECT

KICKBACK

KICKBACK

IMPROPER INSERTION OF SAW
INTO A PREVIOUS CUT–NOSE
HITTING BOTTOM OF CUT

NOSE CONTACT
WITH ANOTHER
LOG OR BRANCH

KICKBACK

MOVING AWAY WHILE CHAIN
IS STILL AT CUTTING SPEED
AND HITS THE SIDE OF THE CUT

Fig. 7 – Know the Four Major Causes of Kickback and Avoid these Situations

Fig. 8 – Chain Saw Tip with Guard

8. Outfit your chain saw with a low-kickback chain.
This chain is less aggressive, so it is less likely to grab material as it rounds the tip of the guide bar. Low-kickback guide bars are also available.

9. Maintain your saw properly.
A sharp, properly tensioned chain is less likely to kickback. Make sure the saw has had proper maintenance before you start out on a job. Remember that the chain will probably need to be resharpened and retensioned in the field, so bring along proper tools.

PERSONAL PROTECTIVE EQUIPMENT

There are many potential hazards when you use a chain saw. Learning and following proper cutting techniques can protect you from most of those hazards. Another important line of defense is the right PPE. Here's what you need to wear to be properly outfitted for the job.

Trim-fitting, Sturdy Work Pants and Shirt
Clothing should have no drawstrings, fringe, loose threads, or other material that might catch on the chain. Long hair should be pulled away from the face and neck and fastened firmly. Never wear jewelry. Pants should have no cuffs so they don't catch sawdust or sparks.

Heavy-Duty Gloves

You'll want to protect your hands from contact with branches and the chain. Regular leatherwork gloves offer some protection, but special chain-saw gloves or mittens are much better. They have extra padding for extra protection and are worth the investment.

Hard Hat

A hard hat protects you from falling branches and possible saw cuts to the head. Special chain-saw hard hats are available that include attached hearing protection and a face shield (Fig. 9).

Fig. 9 – Hard Hat with Built-in Sound-dampening Earmuffs and Face Shield

Safety Glasses

Safety glasses or goggles should always be worn. Make sure your eye protection conforms to the ANSI Z87.1 standard. Even if you wear a face shield, safety glasses should still be worn. The face shield protects your face from flying wood chips; safety glasses or goggles protect your eyes. (See Chapter 2 for more information on eye protection.)

Hearing Protection

Hearing protection is a must. OSHA recommends hearing protection if noise levels exceed 90 decibels (dB). The best new chain saws are 10 times that loud, at a 100 (dB). (Older-model chain saws are often much louder.) Just one hour of exposure to 100 (dB) can cause some permanent hearing loss. Always wear hearing protection when using a chain saw. Again, a chain-saw hard hat with built-in earmuffs is an excellent investment. (See Chapter 2 for more information on hearing protection.)

Heavy-Duty Work Boots

Your footing is very important so make sure boots have good gripping soles. Special chain-saw boots are available. They have steel toes and tops layered with a cut-resistant material for added protection.

The Occupational Safety and Health Administration has rules on required PPE for all employees who use a chain saw. These rules spell out the proper leg, hand, head, eye, and hearing protection that must be worn. Check the current regulations to make sure you are obeying the rules. OSHA's website is www.osha.gov

EXTRA LAYERS OF PROTECTION

Any time a running chain saw comes in contact with the human body, the injury is probably going to be serious. That's why special chain-saw-resistant fabrics have been developed. These fabrics can be found in shirts, gloves, mittens, boots, and chaps made especially for chain-saw users. With these clothing items you'll generally find a tough outer fabric that covers multiple layers of a ballistic nylon or other high-strength fiber. (Similar types of materials are used in bulletproof vests.) If a running chain cuts into this clothing, the layers of material shred and catches on the chain. This absorbs energy and clogs the chain and drive sprocket so the chain stops quickly. It can't prevent every injury, but it does provide the operator with extra layers of protection if a mishap occurs.

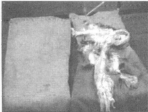

Fig. 10 – Special Chain Saw Chaps (Before and After Contact with a Chainsaw)

Special chain-saw chaps are an excellent way to protect your legs. If a moving chain cuts into the chaps, layers of special ballistic nylon absorb energy and clog the drive sprocket, usually stopping the chain before it causes an injury.

GENERAL CUTTING ADVICE

PROPER MAINTENANCE

The first step in safely using a chain saw is to have it properly maintained. A chain saw will work better and safer if it has sharp teeth, the correct chain tension, proper lubrication, and a well-tuned engine. Adjust the engine idle so when the throttle is released, the engine keeps running but the chain stops.

Maintenance often has to be done in the field. A general guideline is that the chain needs a touch-up sharpening after about two hours of cutting. But if you notice that the chain tends to walk sideways while cutting, or the cut produces powder-like sawdust instead of little wood chips, you need to resharpen and check chain tension.

Your operator's manual is your best source of maintenance information for your saw. If you don't have one, request one from your dealer or the manufacturer.

This Could Be You...Driving into the golf course, Stacey noticed that last night's storm has blown over a small tree near the number 2 tee. She knew it had to get taken care of before the mowing started. So the first thing she did after punching in was grab the chain saw. She remembers looking at the hardhat and chaps, but they hardly seemed worth the effort. This would take only a minute or two. By the time she got to the number 2 tee, she had noted three other spots that needed some cleaning up. Three long hours passed before Stacey got back to the maintenance shed. By then she had a scratch on her face from a falling branch, her ears were ringing, and her left eye was red and swollen from a flying wood chip. Never again, she promised herself, would she take the chain saw out without first putting on proper protective gear.

STARTING THE ENGINE

Since the chain can start moving as soon as the engine starts, it's important to follow the rules for safely starting a chain saw.

Start by placing the saw on a firm level spot on the ground. Make sure the guide bar is not touching anything. Click on the chain brake. This will keep the chain from moving until you are ready to cut. Put your right foot into the rear handle of the saw and grab the front handle with your left hand. Pull the starter rope straight up. Since the chain can start moving as soon as the engine starts (unless brake is set), never allow another person to help you start a chain saw. If either of you slips, the other could be injured.

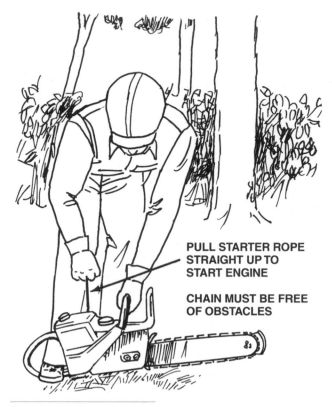

PULL STARTER ROPE STRAIGHT UP TO START ENGINE

CHAIN MUST BE FREE OF OBSTACLES

Fig. 11 – Starting a Chain Saw

NOTE: Be sure to check your operator's manual for other starting procedures specific to your brand of saw.

THE RIGHT GRIP and STANCE

A firm grip is important if you are going to control a chain saw. Grip the front handle bar with your left hand. Hold on tightly, with your thumb and fingers wrapped around the handle. Heavy-duty work gloves or special chain-saw gloves will improve your grip. Put your right hand on the rear handle and throttle trigger. Left-handed operators should follow these instructions as well. When the saw is running, always hold it with both hands.

Have the saw at full throttle before you start cutting. Once contact is made, keep the saw running at full throttle. Let the saw do the cutting. If the chain is sharp, you don't need to apply extra pressure.

When first cutting wood, start small. Make a few trial cuts on small logs. Have logs supported high enough off the ground so the chain easily clears the ground. Never hold the log with your leg or foot.

Always shut off your saw before setting it down. Never carry a running chain saw. If you fall, the saw could spin around and cut you severely. Carry the saw with the guide bar to the rear and the muffler away from you. Mufflers on chain saws can reach 900 degrees F. Use a guide-bar cover, or scabbard, to protect the guide bar, chain, and the operator (Fig. 12).

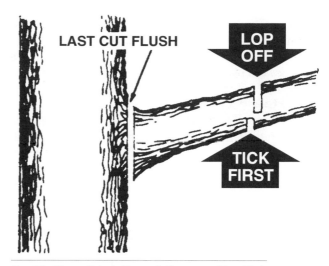

Fig. 13 – Three Cuts to Properly Remove a Tree Limb

Do not trim or cut with the saw above shoulder height. Do not operate a chain saw from a ladder unless you have had special training. If you have higher branches to trim, use a hand-pruning saw.

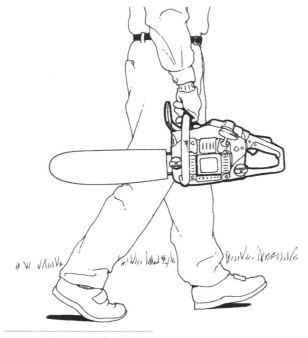

Fig. 12 – Carrying a Chain Saw

TRIMMING

While a chain saw can be a good tool for trimming, small branches pose some special problems. You'll find the chain saw will often skid along thin, whippy growth. This growth can sometimes grab the chain and sharply pull the saw. Pruning small-diameter branches and shrubs are generally best done with hand pruning saws or shears.

For removing larger limbs, a chain saw works great. It takes three cuts to properly remove a tree limb (Fig. 13). The first two cuts will remove most of the limb's weight, making the limb stub easy to cut off. First make a small cut on the underside of a branch, about a foot or more from the trunk. Then lop off the limb from the top, leaving a stub. With the weight of the branch removed, it is now easy to neatly cut the stub off the trunk. Trim off any sharp protrusion of bark or wood so the wound can heal properly. Paint the wound with tar or a tree-wound sealer.

FELLING A TREE

Cutting down a tree takes new levels of skill and understanding. Only after you have mastered steady and even cutting of logs should you attempt to fell a tree.

Before you start, carefully check the situation around the tree you want to remove. Ask yourself these questions:

- **Where do I want the tree to fall?**
- **What is the natural lean of the tree?**
- **Are there any unusually heavy limbs?**
- **Are there any surrounding trees or obstacles?**
- **Any broken or dead branches that could fall during the cut?**
- **What's the wind speed and direction?**

Inexperienced operators should be especially concerned about the wind. Wind can create very serious hazards when cutting down trees. Even on sunny days, the wind can come up suddenly or change direction unexpectedly, causing a tree to fall in the wrong direction. Avoid felling trees on windy days.

A falling tree is a serious safety hazard that can easily kill an operator or a bystander. A simple 6-inch-diameter tree, with leaves, will weigh 500 to 600 pounds.

Also be wary of trees that are rotted or decayed inside, or that are leaning or otherwise under tension. These trees are more likely to snap or split while being cut. That could cause a serious or fatal injury to the operator or bystanders.

Steps to Felling a Tree

1. Determine which direction you want the tree to fall. This is called the line of fall. Take note of the larger branches and wind direction to determine if they will affect the fall.

2. Clear an area around the tree so you have a place to work. Make sure there is a clean pathway for an escape route. This should be in the opposite direction you plan the tree to fall, and at a 45-degree angle away from the planned line of fall. Why a 45-degree angle? In a perfect world the falling tree will always end up perfectly on the planned line of fall. But in some situations, the tree may roll or get hung up as it falls. This could cause the butt end of the falling tree to snap up over the stump along the line of fall. That is why you never want to escape in the exact opposite direction of the fall, but rather at a 45-degree angle away from the line of fall. Since trees don't always fall exactly where planned, there should be an alternative escape route. Always have two escape routes planned – both should be in the opposite direction of the fall, and at a 45 degree angle to the line of fall.

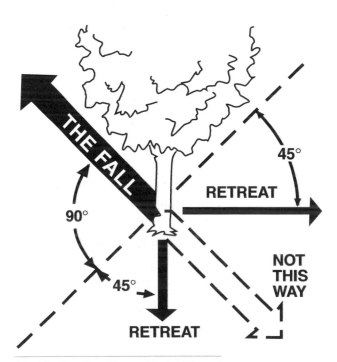

Fig. 14 – Have Two Escape Routes Planned

3. Make a notch on the tree perpendicular to the planned line of fall. (The tree will fall toward the notched side.) The depth of the notch should be about one-third the diameter of the tree.

4. Next, make the felling cut. It will be on the opposite side of the tree from the notch. Cut horizontally, starting at least 2 inches higher than the center of the notch. Do not cut all the way to the notch, but rather leave about 2 inches uncut. This is the hinge that helps control the line of the falling tree. Never cut through the hinge fibers or you could lose control of the line of fall.

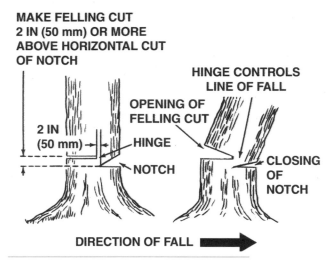

Fig. 15 – The Notch, the Felling Cut and the Hinge

5. The tree will begin to fall as the felling cut approaches the hinge fibers. When the tree starts to fall, remove the saw, shut off the engine, and walk away on your planned escape route. You may need to drive wedges into the felling cut to control the fall. Wedges should be wood or plastic—never use steel wedges, which can damage the chain.

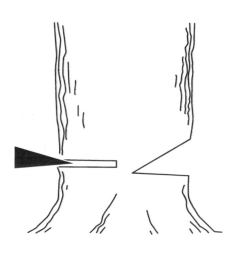

Fig. 16 – Wood or Plastic Wedge

Start Small, Get Help

Felling a tree is serious business. Don't think reading a few paragraphs makes you ready to tackle any tree. The first tree you cut down should be a small one, in a clear open area. As your skill and confidence improves, you can move to bigger trees and bigger challenges.

But remember there are trees and situations that are best left to a professional. For example:

- **Large trees.** Don't tackle trees whose diameter is larger than your guide bar.

- **Dead limbs.** It's not uncommon for dead or broken limbs to fall off the tree while it is being felled. It doesn't take a very big limb crashing to the ground to cause a serious injury.

- **Odd shapes.** If the tree leans away from the line of fall, or if there are heavy branches to one side of the tree, it may not fall where you plan.

- **Obstacles.** If there's a chance the tree may fall on power lines, public roads, buildings, or fences, don't take the chance.

All these situations call for a professional tree expert. If fact, any time you are not quite sure how you should fell a particular tree, it's a sign you should get the help of a professional chain-saw operator.

LIMBING

This is the task of removing branches from a fallen tree. Leave the larger lower limbs to support the log off the ground. Remove limbs by working from the bottom to the top of the tree. Smaller limbs can be removed in one cut; larger limbs should be cut into sections. Roll tree over to remove bottom limbs, or leave them to support the tree until it is bucked.

BUCKING

This is the task of cutting the log up into sections. Make sure you have good footing and can get out of the way if the log should start to roll. On sloping ground, stand above the log rather than below it. If possible, raise the log clear of the ground by using limbs, logs, or chocks. Never let the chain touch the ground. It will damage the chain and may cause kickback.

When the log is supported on one end, cut one-third of the diameter from the underside. This avoids splintering. Then finish the cut from the top.

If the log is supported on both ends, cut one-third of the diameter down from the top. Then make the finish cut from the bottom. The weight of the log will open the cut as you go up from the bottom, keeping the chain from pinching.

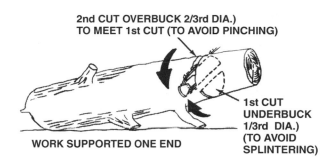

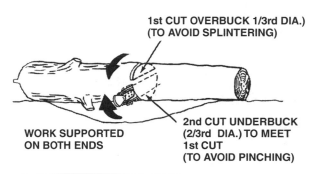

Fig. 17 – Proper Bucking Procedures

This Could Be You (Based on a true story)...a man in Pennsylvania was cutting down trees for firewood in a remote section of a forest. He was working by himself, and no one knew he was going out to cut wood. Things had gone well until a large oak took a funny turn on its way down. The man hadn't planned his escape route well and as the tree came down, the trunk hit him in the leg. His foot was crushed, and worse yet, it was pinned under the trunk. There he lay, alone in the woods, pinned under a fallen tree. He thought a long time about his options. His truck was on a logging road not that far away. But it was unlikely that anyone would find him or his truck for days. Eventually he decided he had to do the unthinkable. He made a tourniquet to limit the bleeding and with a small jackknife he cut off his foot! This gruesome act saved his life. He was able to drag himself to his truck and actually drive to a hospital.

OTHER SAFETY CONCERNS

Fire

Periods of hot, dry weather make leaves and grass a fire hazard. Spilled fuel adds to the danger. Be especially careful when refueling. Refuel on bare ground. Move at least 10 feet (3 m) away from the fuel source before starting the saw. A faulty muffler can provide a spark that could set off a fire. Don't let dry, combustible material contact a hot muffler.

Shattered Wood

If you cut shattered wood, sharp slivers may be caught and flung in the direction of the operator.

Don't Cut Alone

Just as you should never swim alone, it's best if you can cut with a helper in the area. If there is a mishap you'll want someone nearby who could help. At the very least have a cellular phone in your pocket so you can call for help.

Trees and Logs Only

Never use a chain saw to cut wooden objects like old furniture. There may have hidden nails and other metal obstacles.

Major Storm Damage

Working in a blowdown area is very dangerous. Only trained professionals should tackle a job where logs, limbs, and roots are all tangled.

LOG SPLITTERS

Log splitters use hydraulic power to push a wedge through a log. The design is quite simple. Generally the log is placed between the wedge and a stationary plate. The operator activates a hydraulic cylinder that pushes the wedge through the log, splitting it in two. The hydraulic power generally comes from a pump run by a small gasoline engine. Log splitters are handy, but the huge forces they generate can also cause serious injuries.

Fig. 18 – Even Though a Log Splitter is a Simple Machine, it can Cause Serious Injury

COMMON INJURIES

Even though a log splitter is a simple machine, it can cause serious injuries. The most common log splitter injury is crushed hands or feet. The wedge exerts tremendous force onto the log. Body parts caught by the moving wedge will be crushed or amputated.

None of these injuries has to happen. It's easy to avoid all crushing mishaps. Simply keep your hands and feet clear of the log, the wedge, and the stationary plate whenever the cylinder is moving.

Many injuries occur when one person loads the logs and a second person runs the controls. If the loader's hands are not out of the way when the wedge starts moving, a serious injury will result.

A log splitter is a one-person machine. When the same person who loads the logs also runs the controls, the chance of injury is greatly reduced.

But even a single operator can get injured if he tries to do two things at once—namely put the log on with his hands while he hits the control lever with his foot. Use only your hand to operate the control lever. Using your foot or a pull rope to activate the control lever may make it impossible to stop the moving wedge fast enough to avoid an injury.

OTHER SAFETY CONCERNS

Dress Appropriately

Wear safety glasses to protect your eyes from flying splinters of wood. Hearing protection, heavy-duty work clothes, work gloves, and sturdy boots are all recommended as well. Leave jewelry at home, and secure long hair above the shoulder.

Prepare Logs Properly

Have both ends of the logs cut as square as possible. This helps prevent the log from riding out of the splitter when the wedge advances.

Solid Footing

Safe footing is important for operator safety, so only operate the splitter on firm, level ground. Avoid work sites that are slippery, muddy, or icy. Make sure the wheels of the splitter are solidly blocked in place so it doesn't move.

Double Logs

Only split one log at a time. The second log could fly out and injure you.

Hydraulic Leaks

Escaping hydraulic fluid can penetrate skin and cause serious injury – do not touch it. Keep all hydraulic connections tight. If you see leaking fluid, use cardboard or a piece of wood to check for pinhole hydraulic leaks.

Fig. 19 — The Jet Stream or Mist from a Pinhole Leak can Penetrate Flesh

Unattended Splitter

If you leave your log splitter unattended for any time, shut off the engine and take the key, or pull the spark plug wire. Protect children and others who may visit while you are gone.

ADDITIONAL RESOURCES

Chain Saw Safety, Instructional Materials Laboratory, University of Missouri-Columbia, Columbia, MO, ph 573-882-2883

Chain Saw Safety Manual, #OMM955226, Deere & Company, Moline, IL; ph 800-522-7448, or contact your nearest John Deere dealer for a copy.

Chain Saw Safety Manual, (a booklet with the same name as above) is published by Stihl Chainsaws. Contact your nearest Stihl dealer for a copy.

The Forest Industry Safety & Training Alliance (FISTA) offers safety videos, information, and training, ph 800-551-2656, or www.newnorth.net/FISTA

TEST YOURSELF

QUESTIONS - CHAPTER 11

1. List the four major causes of chainsaw-related injuries.

2. What causes kickback?

3. List three ways to prevent kickback and kickback related injuries.

4. List important personal protective equipment you should wear before you use a chainsaw.

5. How do chainsaw-resistant fabrics protect operators?

6. If you are not sure you can safely fell a tree, what should you do?

7. Why should just one person operate a log splitter?

GOLF-COURSE EQUIPMENT

INTRODUCTION

There are many types of equipment found on golf courses. This chapter covers the safety concerns of specialized golf course and fine-turf equipment such as riding and walk-behind reel mowers, bunker rakes, aerators, and vacuums. Other equipment found on golf courses, such as tractors, sprayers, utility vehicles, and rotary mowers, are covered in their own chapters.

Fig. 1 – The Terrain and Wet Working Conditions on Golf Courses Make for Some Special Safety Concerns

Golf courses and their equipment pose some special safety challenges for operators. The terrain is often rolling, with some courses having steep hills or mounds designed into their layouts.

Slick conditions are another challenge. Much of the grounds-maintenance work on golf courses is done in the early morning, before the public arrives. That means the turf is often dew-covered and slippery.

And like other outdoor power equipment, golf course equipment is powerful, with the potential to injure its operators and/or other parties.

SAFETY CONCERNS

These working conditions translate into three of the biggest safety concerns on golf courses. Namely, how to prevent injuries caused by:

- **Wet, slippery conditions**
- **Equipment rollover**
- **Reel mowers**

Let's look at how to safely tackle each of these three areas of concern.

WET, SLIPPERY CONDITIONS

Much of the work on golf courses is done in the early hours of the day when the grass is wet. The combination of the dampness and the finely chopped turf can make the ground and machine platforms very slippery. With this environment, it should come as no surprise that slips and falls are a serious cause of injuries on golf courses.

You can't do much about the moisture, but there are three things you can do to prevent slips and falls.

1. Keep machine platforms clean and clear of debris. Most riding machines have platforms made of material that limits slipping. But a good design won't help much if trash, mud, and old grass are allowed to accumulate on the platforms. It's up to you to keep the platform clean and free of debris.

2. Wear good boots. Footwear should be sturdy and have good gripping soles.

3. Make sure you have good control when you get on or off a machine. Use the machine's steps and steady yourself by grabbing onto a handhold or something secure. Never jump onto or off of a machine.

Fig. 2 – Keep Machine Platforms Clean and Free of Debris

Slips and falls can happen away from equipment as well. Use special care when working on wet turf, or when your boots may have a coating of wet grass trimmings. Take your time and pay attention to your footing.

EQUIPMENT ROLLOVER

By the nature of golf course design, equipment operators often encounter hills and steep slopes. This may be on mowed areas or inside sand traps.

To avoid rollovers, there are three important things you can do:

1. Understand the terrain.

2. Understand your machine.

3. Drive slowly.

Understand the Terrain

To understand the terrain, you'll need to depend on good judgment, and sound advice. Generally, with a riding mower, hills should be mowed up and down the slope. However, this is not necessarily the case on golf courses. The direction you mow will depend on how steep the slope is and the machine you are operating. Make sure you know which direction your supervisor wants hills mowed or sand traps worked. Most golf courses have a mowing plan for every area of the course. Make sure you have clear directions and follow them. Never approach an unknown hill from the top. It may be too steep or have dangerous surprises.

This Could Be You…. Things had not gone well this morning. With two greensmowers broken down, Marti had to race to keep ahead of the first group of golfers. Luckily, she knew a short cut to the 10th green that would save her a few minutes. She had taken the short cut many times with a utility vehicle. It never occurred to her that her riding greensmower might not handle the hilly route as well. She also forgot that she had never driven the hill when dew was on the grass. All these miscalculations hit her at once as she started down the first slope. The mower began to slide sideways down the hill. She was headed right for a sand trap. After a few moments of panic, Marti remembered to lower the cutting units. This slowed the machine so that she came to a halt just 3 feet from the steep edge of the sand trap. She didn't want to think about how her day would have turned out had she not been able to slow down.

Understand the Machine

You must be aware of the specific characteristics of the machine you are operating. Make sure you have read the operator's manual before running your machine. Go over the machine, noting all the safety warning signs. You should also have training from an experienced operator. Make sure you fully understand all the controls before you operate a machine (Fig. 3). If you encounter a potentially dangerous situation, you may need fast reactions.

Fig. 3 – Understand All Controls Before you Operate a Machine

Once you've learned how to run the machine, practice operating it on level ground. If you are new to golf course equipment, you'll find tri-cycle machines and equipment with rear-wheel steer behave quite different from the cars, trucks, or tractors you've driven. Plus, the wet turf can make handling any machine more challenging.

Make sure you understand your machine's limitations before you tackle any slopes. And never approach an unknown hill from the top. It may be too steep for your equipment (Fig. 4).

Fig. 4 – Know the Terrain Before you Mow

Drive Slowly

As outlined in Chapter 5, the faster you drive, the greater are the forces that can cause a rollover. It's always a good idea to drive at a safe speed. But when operating on slopes, you may find that safe speed to be quite slow. Understand the safe operating speeds for different areas of the golf course. Follow these guidelines, and slow down even more if turf conditions limit traction and control. Be especially careful when turning or changing directions on a slope. Watch for holes or hidden obstructions.

Fig. 5 – Use Special Care When Driving a Bunker Rake on a Slope

Use special care when driving or operating a bunker rake on a slope. With bunker rakes there's the added chance of rolling over backward. Do not stop or start suddenly when going uphill or downhill. The sudden change of direction may cause an upset.

Vacuums also pose a special hazard on slopes. That's because as the vacuum's hopper fills, the machine's center of gravity rises. Use extreme caution when operating on slopes. Slow down when making sharp turns or when turning on hillsides.

REEL MOWERS

Reel mowers cut grass using a group of knives (six or more) arranged in the shape of a cylinder. As the reel turns, each knife passes very, very close to a stationary, or bed knife. As the mower moves through the turf, blades of grass are caught between the spinning reel knives and the bed knife, shearing off the grass.

Fig. 6 – When the Reel Spins, Its Knives Slice Past the Bed Knife Shearing Off the Blades of Grass

Reel mowers offer several advantages over conventional rotary mowers. Reel mowers give the operator more control over the length of cut, important on golf courses and ball fields. Since reel mowers slice the grass between the reel knife and the bed knife, there's a cleaner cut, which is healthier for the grass. Plus, reel mowers work better in damp, wet grass. Reel mowers are more expensive to purchase and maintain, and they are more easily damaged if they run into sticks or trash.

Safely Operating a Reel Mower
Before you mow for the first time, you should have read your machine's operator's manual, located all the safety signs on your machine, and had operator training. You should also be familiar with the area you are to mow. Spend some time operating the mower with the reels off to get a feel of how the machine handles.

Before you actually start mowing in an area, look around for debris. Sticks, cans, and other items can damage the reels, or they can be cut and thrown with great force.

This Could Be You...Cito was mowing on the number 17 fairway. The heavy rains of the past few days had left the grass long and wet. He had just started up a long, low hill when the reel clogged and quit turning. Cito shut down the engine, lowered the cutting units, and got off to inspect the reel. There was no sign of debris, just a thick glob of grass. He reached in to clear the plug. But the instant Cito freed the plug of grass; he also freed up the reel. Unknown to Cito, there was residual pressure in the hydraulic lines that power the cutting units. With the plug gone, that residual power made the reel turn. In an instant, the top third of Cito's right index finger lay on the ground.

If the reel hits an object, stop the machine, shut off the engine, and remove the key before inspecting for damage. If the reel is blocked or stalled, keep all body parts away from the cutting edges. Hydraulic pressure in the system could cause the reel to suddenly turn when the blockage is released.

If you can see reel damage, or there are strange noises or vibrations, return your mower to the maintenance area for repairs.

Whenever the engine is running, keep hands and feet away from all moving parts. The reel turns so fast, it may not look like it's moving, but it can easily slice through fingers and toes.

Fig. 7 – Keep All Body Parts Away from Cutting Units when the Engine is Running

When the mower is in transport, you can protect the reels by keeping them raised. But remember lowering the cutting units will lower your center of gravity, thus improving your stability. If you need to transport on grass hills, drive carefully, drive slowly, and lower your cutting units until you are on more-level turf.

When you park your machine for any reason, make sure you follow safety rules. Before dismounting, put the machine in neutral or park, lock the park brake, lower cutting units to the ground, turn off engine, and remove the key. Wait for reels to stop turning before getting off the machine.

When you are finished cutting for the day, wash your machine with care. Give the machine some time to cool, and direct water away from the engine and hydraulic units. Never spray cold water on a hot engine. Be especially careful when cleaning around reels.

Fig. 8 – Make Sure the Engine has Cooled Before Refueling

Make sure the engine has cooled before refueling. Clean up any spilled fuel immediately (Fig. 8).

Remember that reel knives are very sharp. Even when a cutting unit is removed from a machine it can hurt you. Protect your hands with heavy gloves when working with or manually rotating the reel.

OTHER SAFETY CONCERNS

Here are some general safety tips to follow when using golf course equipment.

Wear Proper Clothing
Choose substantial shoes or boots and close-fitting shirt and pants. Avoid dangly jewelry and jackets with drawstrings. These can wrap on a reel or drive resulting in serious injury. Keep long hair securely tucked up in a hat. Check the operator's manual to see if hearing protection is recommended. A hard hat and eye protection are often a good idea.

Inspect the Machine Before you Operate
Be sure hardware is tight, and that shields and guards are in good condition and fastened in place.

Make Sure All Safety Interlocks are Functioning
Safety interlocks may keep the engine from starting if the PTO or reels are engaged, or they may shut off the engine if the operator leaves the seat. These interlocks are there for your protection. If they are not working properly, do not operate the machine until they have been repaired.

Keep Pets and People Out of the Work Area
Stop your machine if anyone enters the area.

Stay Alert
The warm sun, the drone of the engine, and the need to make long, straight passes all contribute to fatigue and drowsiness. Taking short breaks will help you stay awake and alert.

Stay Clear of Moving Parts
Keep hands, feet, clothing, and other objects away from moving parts. Never attempt to remove an obstruction while the engine is running. If anyone enters your work area shut off the machine until he or she has left.

Fig. 9 – Keep Hands and Feet Away from Moving Parts

Avoid Coasting
Some machines will accelerate when going downhill, even when they are in gear and the throttle set low. Be sure you know if the machine you are operating is like this. Use your brakes to control your downhill speed.

Make Adjustments Safely
Engage the parking brake, shut off the engine, remove the key, and wait for the engine and all moving parts to stop. Only then is it safe to dismount and make adjustments. Remember that the turf may be slippery, so watch your footing.

Keep Riders Off
Riders can distract the operator, making it more difficult to safely run the machine. Plus they can easily be thrown off the machine and seriously injured. Never give rides. An extra rider can easily lose his grip and fall off the machine, resulting in serious injuries.

Fig. 10 – Never Give Rides

Avoid High-pressure Fluids

Escaping hydraulic fluid can penetrate the skin, causing serious injury. Never search for a leak using a bare, or even gloved hand. Use a piece of cardboard, or wood, to find the source of the leak. Any fluid injected into the skin must be surgically removed within a few hours, or gangrene may result.

Refuel Carefully

Shut off the engine and wait for it to cool. Be sure you are outside in an open area and that no one is smoking nearby. Never refuel indoors or near an open flame. Fill until the fuel level reaches an inch or so below the filler neck. Refueling at the end of each day's operation helps keep condensation out of the fuel tank.

ADDITIONAL RESOURCES

Turf Maintenance Safety Education Program (booklet/video), The Toro Company, Bloomington, MN

At the Golf Course Superintendents Association of America you'll find information on safety-related books and tapes, as well as upcoming seminars. Call 800-472-7878 or visit www.gcsaa.org

TEST YOURSELF

QUESTIONS - CHAPTER 12

1. Name the three biggest safety concerns for operators of golf course equipment.

2. Name two good ways to prevent slips and falls around golf course equipment.

3. How can a reel mower still be dangerous, even if the engine is shut off?

4. Name three ways to avoid equipment rollovers.

5. Why do turf vacuums become more dangerous as they fill?

SPRAYING EQUIPMENT

INTRODUCTION

Beautiful, weed-free turf isn't something Mother Nature does on her own. But thanks to **fertilizers**, **insecticides**, and **herbicides**, turf professionals can make it happen. Applying these chemicals can be done easily and safely if you follow directions and take precautions. But take shortcuts, and you'll risk serious injury not only to yourself but also to the environment and people living in your community.

This Could Be You...Kiana felt lucky to have a summer job at Rock Creek Country Club. She liked working outdoors, even if she had to get up before the sun. This morning she was on spraying duty—her first time driving the big sprayer. It was still dark and foggy when she set out to spray the number 12 fairway. She had been to number 12 before, but never in the dark. And the fog made it only worse. Kiana was sure she was almost there when the paved cart path suddenly ended. That wasn't right. Maybe she had missed a turn and was on 14. That had to be what happened—she could hear the rush of Rock Creek right behind her. "I'll just turn the sprayer around," she thought. But as she started to turn, the ground suddenly fell away. The sprayer was sliding down some kind of slope, and she couldn't do anything about it. All she knew was that she was sitting on a machine full of 200 gallons of herbicide, and the sound of Rock Creek was getting closer and closer.

IMPORTANT SAFETY CONCERNS

Spraying-related mishaps generally fall into two categories—mechanical and chemical. Mechanical mishaps are those where the operator is injured by the spraying equipment. The most common mechanical-related incidents involve:

- **Operator entanglements**
- **Rollovers.**

Chemical-related injuries are caused by exposure to pesticides. These mishaps often involve:

- **Improper operator protection**
- **Failure to follow mixing and application directions**
- **Chemical spills.**

In this chapter on spraying equipment, we'll briefly look at how to prevent mechanical mishaps. Then we'll look at how to prevent **pesticide** injuries by limiting exposure to chemicals. We'll study product labels, Material Data Safety Sheets, signal words, pesticide exposure through the body, personal protective equipment, and spills. The chapter will close with information on pesticide storage and transport and other safety concerns.

PREVENTING MECHANICAL MISHAPS

Spraying equipment comes in various sizes, from small, hand-operated sprayers that hold just a few gallons to large, self-propelled sprayers that can carry hundreds of gallons of chemicals. The risk of having a machine-related injury varies with the size of the sprayer.

Fig. 2 – Larger Sprayers Pose a Greater Risk of Machine-related Injuries

ROLLOVERS

Avoiding sprayer rollovers is not quite so simple. That's because rollovers are caused by a combination of factors—how steep the terrain is, how fast you are driving, how slippery the turf, and the center of gravity of the machine you are driving.

It's important to remember that a tank full of chemicals raises the sprayer's center of gravity and affects the vehicle's traction and braking. The higher the center of gravity, the easier it is for a vehicle to roll over. And the more the unit weighs, the longer it will take to slow down and stop. (A 200-gallon tank full of chemicals adds about 1,600 pounds to the weight of a sprayer.) Add wet, slippery turf to the situation, and even gentle slopes can pose special safety concerns.

Here are some basic rules:

- **Slow down**—driving slowly makes it easier to keep control of the vehicle.

- **Drive up and down hills**—driving across a slope increases the chance of a rollover.

- **Turn slowly**—this is especially true if turning on a slope. It's best to avoid any turns when driving on slopes.

- **Scout the area**—make sure you know the terrain you are going to spray. The time to discover a steep hill is not when you are loaded with 1,600 pounds of pesticide solution.

Remember, when conditions change, your driving must also change. A hill that is no challenge to an empty utility vehicle on a hot, dry afternoon may be impossible to safely navigate if the tank is full and the grass is wet. Take extra precaution when spraying or transporting with a full tank, especially on hilly terrain.

For more information on rollovers, center-of-gravity and safe driving of sprayer vehicles, review Chapters 5 and 14.

Fig. 1 – Hand-operated Sprayers Pose Little Mechanical Risk but do put the Operator Close to the Chemicals Being Sprayed (Photo courtesy of Gempler's, Inc.)

Backpack and small, hand-held sprayers are usually powered by the operator and pose little mechanical risk. The greatest concern with these sprayers is the exposure to pesticides. That's because the operator is closer to the chemicals being sprayed and the plants that have already been sprayed.

Larger sprayers present a greater risk of mechanical injury for two reasons. They are powered by engines so there's the risk of the operator getting entangled in a drive. Secondly, the large volume of pesticides these sprayers can carry increases the risk of rollovers.

Avoiding operator entanglement is straightforward—simply stay away from moving parts. To do this it's important you understand your machine and where moving parts are located. Thoroughly read the operator's manual for both the sprayer and the vehicle that carries or tows the sprayer. If the sprayer requires adjustment or service, always shut off the engine and let all moving parts come to a complete stop before getting out of the driver's seat.

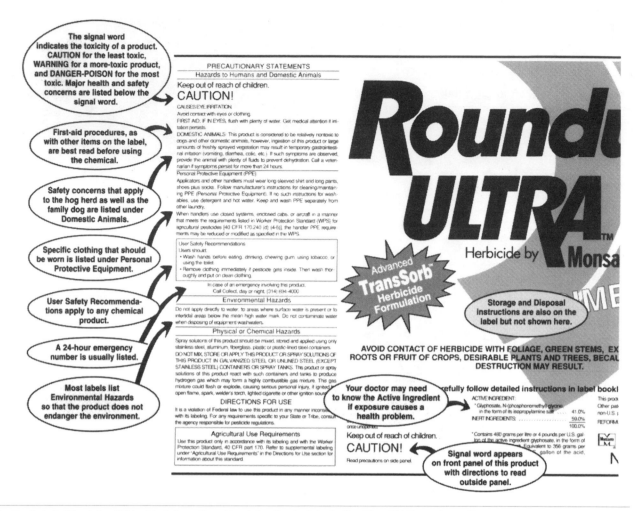

Fig. 3 – Labels Give lots of Valuable Information About the Product, Including First Aid Procedures, Recommended PPE, and a List of Environmental Hazards

PREVENTING CHEMICAL MISHAPS

Any time you work with chemicals, even common household chemicals, there is a risk. If you've ever splashed soap into your eyes, you know this firsthand. The key to preventing chemical-related injuries is to limit your exposure to the chemical. **Limit the exposure and you'll limit the risk.**

To limit exposure, it's important you know the recommended Personal Protective Equipment (PPE) and other clothing you should wear, as well as proper handling techniques for the pesticide you'll be applying. This information is found on the product label. The label lists only the minimum PPE that is required — you can go a step further and wear more protection. For example, wear chemical resistant gloves rather than waterproof gloves.

PRODUCT LABELS

Look over the Roundup ULTRA® product label (Fig. 3). Callouts show the types of information you'll find on a pesticide label. You'll see that the label gives you:

- **A product signal word describing how toxic the product is**
- **A list of protective clothing that should be worn**
- **Directions for proper use of the product**
- **User safety recommendations**
- **Safety concerns for animals**
- **A 24-hour emergency phone number**
- **A list of environmental hazards**
- **First aid procedures in case of a mishap.**

Because the label has so much important information, it must stay attached to the chemical container. If a label is ripped or falls off a container, it should be taped back on. That way the label is available for anyone working with the product. Plus, if there is an emergency, the product safety information will be easy to find.

MATERIAL SAFETY DATA SHEETS

Besides the label, there's another place you can find safety information on pesticides. It's the Material Safety Data Sheet (MSDS). By U.S. law, every employer must keep an MSDS on file for every hazardous chemical the firm uses. These files must be available to all employees who could come in contact with the chemical.

The MSDS generally has all the information found on the label, plus:

- **Physical and chemical characteristics of the pesticide**

- **Fire and explosion hazard data**

- **Detailed toxicity**

- **Symptoms from prolonged exposure to the chemical**

- **Control measures in case of a spill**

It's important to know where your employer keeps the MSDS files. If an emergency happens, you will want to have quick access to this information. Plus if you work around chemicals and have any unexplained illnesses, you'll want to read the MSDS to see if the illness could be related to chemical exposure.

SIGNAL WORDS

Every chemical label must display the signal word that indicates how toxic the product is. By understanding these signal words—**Danger-Poison**, **Warning**, and **Caution**— you'll have a good indication of a product's potential risk.

Highly toxic chemicals that are corrosive to the eyes and skin carry the signal word **Danger-Poison**. These products will also have the skull-and-crossbones symbol on the label. Swallowing less than a teaspoon can kill a 150-pound person.

Chemicals that could severely irritate the skin and eyes for a week or longer carry the signal word **Warning**. Ingesting a tablespoon of this class of chemicals can be fatal.

Chemicals that result in only mild skin and eye irritation carry the signal word **Caution**. It would take swallowing up to a pint of this type of substance to be fatal. For persons weighing less than 150 pounds, or children, smaller amounts can cause illness or deaths.

PESTICIDE EXPOSURE TO THE BODY

Now you may be thinking, who would be stupid enough to eat even a teaspoon of a herbicide or insecticide? It turns out there are ways for a pesticide to get into your body that don't involve eating a foul-tasting chemical. Ways that can easily happen without you knowing.

PESTICIDE EXPOSURE

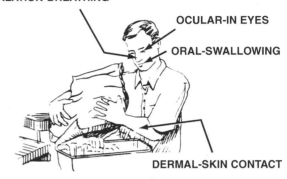

Fig. 4 – Pesticides Can Enter Your Body Through Four Types of Exposure

The four ways pesticides can be taken into your body are:

- **Ocular exposure**—when you get a pesticide in your eyes

- **Dermal exposure**—when you get a pesticide on your skin

- **Inhalation exposure**—when you breathe in a pesticide

- **Oral exposure**—when you swallow a pesticide

If you understand how these exposures typically occur, you'll be better able to avoid exposure.

Eye exposures is often caused by:

- **Splashing pesticides into eyes, which can easily happen while mixing**

- **Applying chemicals during windy weather without eye protection**

- **Rubbing eyes or forehead with contaminated gloves or hands**

- **Pouring granules or powder chemicals without eye protection.**

Dermal exposure is often caused by:

- **Wearing inadequate PPE while handling chemicals**
- **Not washing hands after handling pesticides or their containers**
- **Wearing pesticide-contaminated gloves or other clothing**
- **Applying pesticides in windy weather**
- **Splashing or spraying pesticides on unprotected skin**
- **Touching pesticide-treated surfaces.**

Inhalation exposure is often caused by:

- **Breathing vapors, dust, or mist while handling chemicals**
- **Using the wrong respirator for the chemical you are working with**
- **Using a respirator that has not been properly maintained and has filters or cartridges full of chemicals or dust**
- **Using an improperly fitted respirator**
- **Prolonged contact with pesticides in a closed or poorly ventilated space.**

Oral exposure is often caused by:

- **Not washing hands before eating, drinking, smoking, or chewing tobacco**
- **Eating in an area that's contaminated with pesticides**
- **Accidentally splashing pesticides into your mouth.**

While none of these common causes of exposure are likely to give you a lethal dose of chemicals in one shot, they can add up over time to a combined dose that will make you sick or give you long-term health problems.

*Fig. 5 – **Don't Touch!** Until you Have Rinsed and Removed Your Protective Gloves, Resist Touching Anything that You Don't Want Contaminated — Including Steering Wheels, Doorknobs, Cigarettes, Food and Drinks. Especially Resist Touching Your Face. Studies Show The Average Adult Touches His or Her Face 14 Times an Hour.*

It's also good to remember that certain parts of the body absorb chemicals much faster than other parts. For example, the groin can absorb chemicals very quickly, making it important to wash your hands before you go to the bathroom.

The forehead, scalp, and ear canal all absorb pesticides quite quickly. So scratching your head, or wiping sweat from your forehead, is a serious exposure concern.

Finally, if a worker is taken to a doctor due to feeling ill or overcome while working with chemicals, take along a copy of the label or the MSDS. That will aid the doctors diagnosis and treatment.

PERSONAL PROTECTIVE EQUIPMENT

Earlier we learned that the way to avoid chemical injury is to limit your exposure to pesticides. Limit the exposure and you'll limit the risk. But as we've just discussed, it's relatively easy to become exposed to the chemicals you work around. The way around this dilemma is the proper use of personal protective equipment.

Personal protective equipment (PPE) is specially designed to protect your body from being exposed to chemicals. The type of gear you should wear is spelled out on the product label. While a general discussion of PPE is in Chapter 2, the following equipment is of special interest to persons applying pesticides.

GLOVES

For pesticide work gloves should be unlined and waterproof or chemical resistant. Never use cotton or leather gloves because they can absorb chemicals and actually increase exposure. There is an exception. If you are working with roses or thorny plants, you can wear leather gloves but chemical-resistant gloves underneath. For most typical pesticide applications, nitrile gloves in a 20-mil thickness work well. Gloves should be at least 12 inches long from the fingertip to the cuff. (Be sure to check the pesticide label for exact recommendations.)

Before removing your gloves, rinse them thoroughly under running water. This will remove many contaminants, but it is impossible to remove them all. That's why it's best to discard gloves at the end of each use. Remove a glove by grabbing at the cuff end and pulling it off inside out. This will keep any contaminants inside. Put the gloves in a resealable freezer bag and throw them away. It may seem wasteful to discard perfectly usable gloves, but it's a simple, low-cost way to protect the health of people who work around chemicals. If purchased in quantity, these gloves are not very expensive.

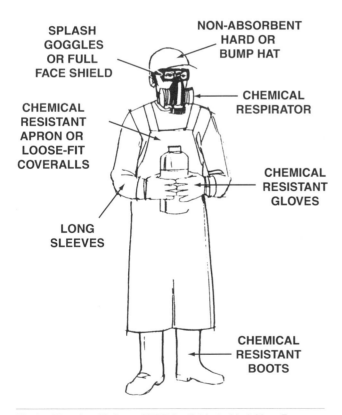

Fig 6 – There's a Variety of PPE Available to Limit Your Exposure to Pesticides. Always Follow Label Recommendations

GOGGLES or FACE SHIELDS

Wear tight-fitting, nonfogging, chemical-splash goggles or a full face shield when pouring, mixing, or applying chemicals. Clean the equipment daily to prevent any chemical buildup.

BOOTS

When handling or applying chemicals wear unlined, light-weight rubber vinyl boots that cover your ankles. Wear pant legs on the outside so pesticides cannot drain down into the boots. The boots should be washed daily and dried thoroughly inside and out to remove pesticide residues.

RESPIRATORS

A respirator prevents inhalation of toxic chemicals, but only if it is properly fitted and properly maintained. Respirators need to fit snuggly at all face-contact points to prevent chemical vapors from bypassing the filters. Remember, a beard or other facial hair may make it impossible to get the snug fit you need. Keep your face clean shaven if you need to wear a respirator.

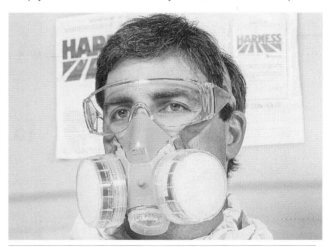

Fig. 7 – A Properly Fitted and Maintained Respirator can Protect you From Toxic Vapors, Mist, and Dust
(Photo courtesy of Gempler's, Inc.)

The cartridges used in respirators protect against specific chemical gasses and vapors. Be sure to use the type of respirator called for on the pesticide label. Don't take chances with your lungs.

Respirator maintenance is very important. Cartridges should be changed after eight hours of use, or sooner if you detect pesticide odor while wearing the respirator. If breathing becomes difficult during spraying, get some fresh, clean air and change the cartridges. The face piece should be washed daily with soap and water, rinsed, and dried with a clean cloth. Store the respirator in a clean, dry place away from pesticides. A tightly closed plastic bag works well for storage.

HEAD and BODY COVERINGS

Since the scalp absorbs pesticides quite readily, it's a good idea to wear waterproof head gear, even if it's not required on the product label. Never use cotton or felt hats that could actually absorb chemicals. To protect your body, always wear a long-sleeve shirt and long pants. For greater protection, consider special chemical-application coveralls. Some come with a hood to protect the head and neck from chemical exposure. Again, the pesticide label will give you clothing advice. Always consider this advice to be the minimum protection you need. It's no sin to take extra precautions.

CLOTHING CARE

Care and cleaning of personal clothes and protective garments are very important. Wear clean clothes every day you spray pesticides. If chemicals get on your clothing, get clean clothes immediately. Wearing tainted clothes until the end of the day only gives you more exposure.

Fig. 8 – Wear Clean Clothes Everyday You Spray. Change Clothes Immediately If Pesticides Spill on Garments

Be sure not to contaminate other areas with your soiled clothes. Store these clothes separately in a plastic bag if washing cannot be immediate. For best pesticide removal, hose them off before washing, or pre-rinse them in a tub or the pre-rinse cycle of your washing machine. Dispose of the rinse water and refill the washer for detergent washing. Wash pesticide soiled clothes separately from other laundry in hot water with heavy detergent. Use the regular wash cycle with maximum agitation, not a shorter or more gentle one. Repeated washing may further reduce residues. Afterward, run your washer through a complete cycle without clothes to rinse away any residues. Washing with the family laundry increases the chance of contaminating other clothes. Line dry clothes or use high temperature setting on the automatic dryer. The sun may help degrade and the high heat help volatilize pesticide residues.

If concentrated pesticide is spilled on your clothes, remove the soiled garments immediately and discard. Research shows that even after 10 washings, harmful chemical residue can remain in fabrics.

This Could Be You...Richard hadn't bothered to put on rubber gloves when he filled the sprayer, and it didn't bother him one bit. Those gloves made his hands sweat and his fingers clumsy. And anyway, there was no way he could have fixed that leaking spray nozzle wearing those bulky gloves. His hands were dry now, and the spray no longer burned that cut on his right hand. What was the big deal with gloves anyway? He liked going with bare hands, and he liked that it was Monday. The golf course was closed, and there was nobody to see him smoke, or take a leak. He even had his lunch along and could enjoy his sandwich under that big oak by the number 5 green. It was just a beautiful day and nothing was going to ruin it.

SPILLS

Even when proper procedures are followed, pesticide spills can occur. Knowing what steps to take will prevent injury to yourself, your fellow workers, and the environment.

There are three things to remember in case of a spill:

- **Control**
- **Contain**
- **Cleanup**

CONTROL

The first step is to control or stop the spill. Do this as quickly as possible. This could be as simple as closing a dripping valve or putting a leaky container inside a bucket. The goal is to limit how much chemical is spilled.

While it is important to control a spill promptly, be sure to first protect yourself by putting on protective clothing. Fast action is needed but don't leave yourself open to unnecessary chemical exposure.

CONTAIN

Contain the spill by limiting the contaminated area. With a liquid you might make a dam with dirt, or better yet with an absorbent material like cat litter. With a dry chemical, you might rope off the area so no one can walk or drive through the spill.

Fig. 9 – Use a Dike and Absorbent Material Like Cat Litter to Keep a Spill From Spreading. Always Put on Protective Gear Before Tackling a Spill

If a spill can't be contained, divert it away from drains or waterways. Never hose down a spill area. This simply contaminates more area and makes cleanup more difficult.

CLEANUP

Cleanup and other emergency procedures are spelled out on the MSDS. To properly clean up a spill, workers need to be trained in procedures and proper use of protective equipment. While cleanup is important, it's fast action at the control and contain stages that will keep a small spill from becoming a big one.

PESTICIDE STORAGE AND TRANSPORT

Any firm that uses pesticides needs a place to store them. But unlike most company supplies, these chemicals have the potential to cause serious harm to workers and the environment. That why it's so important to take extra steps to properly store and handle these products.

The ideal storage site is a separate building that is heated, ventilated, and can be locked. A dedicated storage building makes it easier to control access, easier to eliminate cross contamination, and easier to handle fires or other serious incidents.

If a separate building is not practical, have a locked storage compartment or room inside an existing building. This area should be kept clean, dry, and ventilated. Adequate lighting is important so labels are easy to read and spills or leaks easy to see.

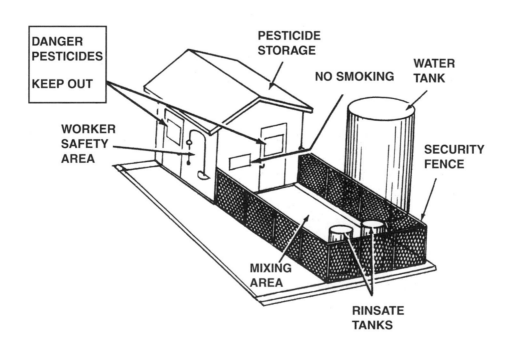

Fig. 10 – The Best Place to Store Pesticides is in a Separate Building That Controls Access and Limits the Chance for Spills

The floor of any pesticide storage site should be made of sealed concrete or some other non-porous, easy-to-clean material. Wood, soil, gravel, or other absorbent floors are difficult or impossible to decontaminate if a leak or spill happens.

Do not store pesticides with other products or chemicals. Certain pesticides and fertilizers can react chemically and result in fire. Never store pesticides near food, seed, or personal protective equipment for fear of contamination.

Store all chemicals in their original containers. Putting pesticides in new containers greatly increases the chance that they could be misused, or that proper safety precautions or disposal recommendations could be ignored. Never remove labels from chemical containers. Read and follow storage requirements explained on the label.

TRANSPORTATION
Transporting chemicals brings about a new set of safety concerns. Containers used during transport must be labeled. This labeling can be either the original product labeling or service-container labeling. Service-container labeling must have the name and address of the person responsible for the container, the common name of the pesticide, and the signal word from the original label.

Make sure pesticide containers are secured in the upright position and all caps are tightly closed. Never transport pesticides in the same compartment with people, food, or animal feed.

Consult your local highway patrol for local or state regulations regarding pesticide transport.

OTHER SAFETY CONCERNS

Container disposal. Chemical containers should be triple rinsed, with the rinse water added to the sprayer tank. Follow state or local regulations for container disposal. Never burn empty chemical containers and never reuse chemical containers for some other purpose.

People and pets in work area. Stop your machine if a person or a pet enters the spraying or mixing area. Some pesticides may restrict reentry to the sprayed area for a length of time. Make sure the area is properly posted.

Pesticide drift. Drift occurs when a chemical sprays blow onto places it's not wanted. When spraying near the property of others, or near areas that shouldn't get sprayed, be aware of the possibility of drift. Do not spray near these areas on windy days. Make sure drift doesn't land on you and increase your pesticide exposure.

Dangerous products. Reduce the risks to spray crews by using less-toxic and less-concentrated pesticides. Consider premixed or ready-to-use formulations, and always buy the least-toxic product that will do the job.

ADDITIONAL RESOURCES
Rely on safety suppliers for equipment or advice. Check the Yellow Pages under safety equipment, or contact mail order firms such as Gempler's 800-382-8473.

There's lots of safety-related information at the National Ag Safety Database www.cdc.gov/niosh/nasd/nasdhome.html.

Rules, regulations, and PPE advice can be found at the Occupational Safety & Health Administration Web Site www.osha.gov.

TEST YOURSELF

QUESTIONS - CHAPTER 13

1. Why do small, handheld or backpack sprayers pose a special risk to the operator?

2. List five things found on a pesticides's label.

3. List four additional things you could find on an MSDS.

4. Give two reasons a chemical should always be kept in its original container.

5. List the four ways chemicals can get into your body.

6. What is the best way to limit your risk of being injured by a chemical?

7. List the three things to remember in case of a chemical spill.

8. Why is it important for a chemical-storage area to have good lighting?

UTILITY VEHICLES

INTRODUCTION

Utility vehicles are off-road work machines designed to carry cargo and sometimes passengers. They generally have a top speed of about 20 mph. These vehicles should not be confused with recreational ATVs or "four-wheelers" that can go much faster and have little or no room for cargo. While most utility vehicles are powered by gasoline or diesel engines, some are electric, powered by rechargeable batteries.

Fig. 1 – Utility Vehicles are Handy Work Tools for Golf Courses and Construction Sites

Because utility vehicles are easy to operate, it's tempting for workers to drive off with little or no training. This is a serious mistake. Lack of experience is a major cause of mishaps. Operators who are not familiar with the handling or limitations of utility vehicles can get themselves into trouble fast.

All drivers should be required to read the operator's manual and have driving lessons before they operate a utility vehicle unsupervised. This operator training should pay special attention to hills, turning, operating speed, and cargo loads. As you'll see, these factors all play important roles in utility-vehicle incidents.

This Could Be You…Gordon knew he was in trouble. This load of bark was supposed to be delivered to the landscape crew 40 minutes ago. It wasn't his fault the stupid utility vehicle had had a dead battery. His best hope for getting there fast was to cut across the hill behind the number 3 green. The hill was pretty steep, but he had driven the slope several times before without a problem. As he started up the hill, he could hear the engine groan. Maybe this wet bark was heavier than he thought. He turned a little to cut more across the side of the hill—so far so good. But suddenly the vehicle started to slide on the wet turf. Gordon overreacted, he knew that now, making a sharp turn down the hill to get out of the skid. It happened almost like slow motion, the bark flying, the machine going over on its side, the sensation of flying. The next thing Gordon knew, he was lying in a pile of wet bark, his legs pinned under the weight of his upside-down vehicle.

IMPORTANT SAFETY CONCERNS

Although driving a utility vehicle can feel like fun, it's important to take these machines seriously. They are designed for tough off-road work, so they can get you into locations and situations that are dangerous. And since these machines can carry cargo, their handling will change with the cargo you haul.

Most utility-vehicle mishaps fall into four categories:

- **Side rollovers**
- **Loss of control**
- **Tipping backward**
- **Rider injuries**

All of these situations can be avoided with proper operator training.

In the first three types of incidents—side rollovers, loss of control, and tipping backward—the cargo you carry can play an important role. So let's first look at how cargo affects utility-vehicle handling and stability.

CARGO CONCERNS

Whenever you put something in a utility vehicle's cargo bed, you raise the vehicle's center of gravity. (For more information on center of gravity, see Chapter 5.) The more weight you add, the more you raise the center of gravity, and the easier it is for that machine to tip.

Fig. 2 – Heavy Loads Increase the Distance it Takes to Stop. Slow Down so You Have Complete Control

Heavy loads also increase a vehicle's stopping distance. The heavier the load the easier it is to lose control of the vehicle. That's why it's so important for you to adjust your driving to the load you are carrying. Heavy loads mean you must drive slowly and turn carefully.

You'll also need to adjust the load you carry to the route you'll be driving. If you need to drive over wet turf, mud, or hills, you'll want to lighten your load. Filling a vehicle to capacity and then driving on steep hills or slick ground is a prescription for an serious mishap.

How the load is placed in the cargo bed also affects vehicle handling. Loads should be evenly distributed. If the load is stacked to one side, it increases the chance of a side rollover.

Fig. 3 – If the Load is Piled to One Side or Shifts While You Drive, it Increases the Chance of a Rollover

It's also important to secure loads in the cargo box. Tie down heavy items such as pipe or landscape timbers that can shift during turns. Material that shifts in the cargo box increases the chance of a mishap.

Read the vehicle's operator's manual and follow load limits. Just because the cargo box is large enough to hold a load doesn't mean you can haul that load safely.

ROLLOVERS AND LOSS OF CONTROL

We've just seen how cargo loads can cause problems. Now let's look at other important factors. Since rollovers and loss of control are caused by similar situations, we'll discuss them together.

Any time an operator loses control of a utility vehicle, it's likely that at least one of these factors was involved—high speed, sharp turns, or steep hills. Pay special attention to these three factors and you'll limit your chances of having a serious mishap.

HIGH SPEED

Many utility-vehicle rollovers could be avoided if drivers just slowed down. Driving fast greatly increases the chance of a rollover. How fast is too fast? It is impossible to say. It all depends on the load, the terrain, and the ground conditions. Ask your supervisor for advice on safe speeds. Experienced drivers know it makes sense to play it safe and drive slowly.

SHARP TURNS

Sharp turns are another important cause of rollovers, and speed often plays a role. The faster you turn, the greater the side forces are that cause a rollover. (For more information on centrifugal force and turns, see Chapter 5.) That's why it's so important to slow down while turning. Again, it is impossible to say how fast is too fast. Just remember no one ever lost control of a utility vehicle by driving too slow.

HILLS

Driving on slopes is just part of the job at many golf courses and construction sites. But driving on slopes also increases the chance of a rollover. That's why it's important to take special precautions.

Drive up and down hills rather than across the slope. The steeper the hill, the more important this rule.

Fig. 4 – Use Extreme Caution When Driving Near a Steep Drop Off or Ravine

Turning on a hill also increases the chance of a rollover. It's best to avoid all turns when driving on a hillside. Instead, drive to the top or bottom of the hill and then make your turn.

Remember that some utility vehicles, especially those with belt-drive transmissions, will free wheel or speed up when going down a hill. When driving down any hill, be ready to gently apply the brakes to slow down. Never panic by slamming on the brakes. This could put you into a skid that you cannot control. Also never try to turn out of a rapid coast down a hill. This just increases the chance of a rollover. Instead, just gently apply the brakes and drive down the hill slowly.

Be extra careful when driving near steep drop-offs or ravines. Here any careless driving or loss of control could end in a very serious injury. Avoid these situations if you can. If they can't be avoided, use extra care as you drive.

Rough ground can also contribute to rollover mishaps. Watch for holes, rocks, roots, and other hidden hazards. Big bumps or dips can induce a rollover, especially if you are driving too fast.

Fig. 5 – Pay Attention for Big Bumps or Holes That Could Bounce Your Vehicle Over. Drive Slowly and Watch Where You Are Going

When there's work to get done and you are in a hurry, it's tempting to take shortcuts—to drive the shortest route or to drive a little faster or to turn a little sharper. But any of these shortcuts can lead to a utility vehicle that is out of control. And that can lead to an incident that results in serious injury or death.

TIPPING BACKWARD

Tipping backward often catches operators totally by surprise. It can happen so quickly, that there is often no chance to react. Fortunately, these mishaps can be prevented if you avoid certain situations.

Fig. 6 – Never Let Rear Tires Hang Over the Edge of a Loading Dock or Ravine

One cause of tipping backward is backing up too far over a loading dock or ravine. This often happens while dumping material. Never allow the vehicle's rear tires to hang over the edge. Without all the vehicle's wheels on the ground, a load in the cargo box could cause the vehicle to flip backward.

A tipping-backward mishap can also happen when coasting backward down a hill. If you back down a hill at a high rate of speed and suddenly slam on the brakes, you can cause the whole vehicle to flip over backward. This can happen if your vehicle is trying to climb a steep hill and runs out of power or traction.

The danger begins when you start back down the hill. Many utility vehicles will speed up, or free wheel, when going down a hill, even if you have the vehicle in gear. If this happens, gently apply the brakes and coast slowly down the hill. Never try to turn out of a downhill descent or you may roll the vehicle. Just gently apply the brakes and coast down the hill slowly. When you are again on level ground, it will be safe to turn and find a safer route to travel.

Fig. 7 – Never Slam on the Brakes When Speeding Backwards Down a Hill

RIDER INJURIES

Some utility vehicles can carry passengers, but only if the manufacturer has provided a seat for each person. Never haul extra people in the cargo box or on the running boards. If there isn't an approved seat, there shouldn't be a rider.

Even passengers in seats need to take precautions. Rough terrain can bounce passengers out of the vehicle. Use provided handholds and anticipate bumps.

This Could Be You…Dawn knew hauling extra riders was against the rules, but everybody did it, especially if no one was watching. She had just finished picking up the equipment from the track meet when Jason appeared looking for a ride up to the parking lot. Amy was already in the one passenger seat, so Jason stood on the running board and off they went. It wasn't long before Jason was pretending he was riding a stagecoach, hanging on to the utility vehicle with one hand and shooting imaginary villains with the other. Dawn was laughing so loud she never noticed the starting block that was lying in the roadway. She was going fast when she hit it, and the force bounced Jason into the air. When he came down, his foot missed the running board. His lost his grip, and his foot went under the rear tire. As Dawn hit the brakes, all she could hear was Jason screaming in pain.

OTHER SAFETY CONCERNS

Entanglements. Keep hands, feet, and clothing away from a running engine and power-driven parts. Entanglement with a rotating driveline can cause serious injury or death. Never make adjustments unless the vehicle is turned off and the key removed.

Losing cargo. Secure cargo in the box. It's easy for loose equipment and supplies to bounce out of the box and injure co-workers or bystanders.

Fig. 8 – Make Sure Cargo Can't Bounce Out of the Vehicle and Injure Others

Battery explosions. Recharge batteries carefully. All recharging batteries give off hydrogen gas. Hydrogen gas is explosive in concentrations as little as 4 percent. If you are recharging a battery-powered vehicle, there must be adequate ventilation to disperse the hydrogen or a deadly explosion could occur. A minimum of five air changes per hour is generally recommended. Consult your operator's manual for more detailed advice.

Carbon monoxide. Carbon monoxide is an invisible and odorless gas that can cause sickness or death. Never run a gasoline or diesel utility vehicle indoors. If you must run the engine in an enclosed area, vent fumes with an **exhaust pipe extension**.

High-pressure fluids. Some utility vehicles have high-pressure hydraulic systems. Escaping fluid can penetrate the skin causing serious injury. Relieve pressure before making any repairs or adjustments.

Hauling a vehicle. Shut off fuel before loading. Tie down the vehicle with straps, chains, or cables. (See Chapter 15 for more information.)

Parking. When parking the vehicle, find a flat spot, turn off the engine, set the parking brake, and remove the key.

Tire pressure. Follow tire pressure guidelines in the operator's manual and check pressure regularly. If tires appear to be low on air, it may be that you are overloading the vehicle.

TEST YOURSELF

QUESTIONS - CHAPTER 14

1. What are the four major causes of utility vehicle mishaps?

2. In what ways does a heavy load affect the handling of a utility vehicle?

3. Name three good ways to limit the chance of a rollover.

4. Why is it especially dangerous to back down a hill with a loaded utility vehicle?

TRANSPORTING OUTDOOR POWER EQUIPMENT

INTRODUCTION

Transporting equipment is a necessity for most landscape and grounds-care firms. Transporting typically involves loading equipment onto a trailer and towing the trailer with a truck.

Since transporting involves moving thousands of pounds of grounds-care equipment at highway speeds, any mishap could be serious. The end result is often major property damage and/or injuries. There are four common types of equipment-transport incidents:

- **Losing control of the truck or tow vehicle**
- **Losing equipment from the trailer**
- **Losing the trailer**
- **Loading and unloading mishaps**

In this chapter we'll look at what you can do to avoid these problems. Plus, we'll discuss how to safely transport fuel for your equipment.

Fig. 1 – One of the Keys to Safe Equipment Transport is a Properly Sized and Equipped Trailer Matched to a Good Tow Vehicle

This Could Be You...Luis couldn't believe he missed that turn. Now he had to find a place to turn around to get back on the right road. He was so upset he forgot for a moment that he was pulling a loader tractor on his trailer. And he forgot that he had never double checked the tractor's tie downs on that trailer. None of that mattered right now because Luis saw just what he was looking for—a big, empty parking lot. He slammed on the brakes and turned sharply into the lot. After that everything happened pretty quickly. First he felt the jerk on the truck as the trailer tire bounced up over the curb...he had turned too tight. Then he heard the crunching sound as the trailer gouged into a power pole that stood at the edge of the parking lot...man, had he turned too sharp. And then came the big thud, as the falling tractor hit the pavement. Luis's eye darted to the rear-view mirror and his heart sank. Twenty thousand dollars of equipment lying in a pool of diesel fuel and oil.

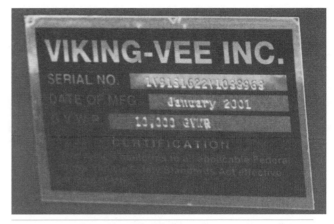

Fig. 2 – The Serial-Number Plate on the Trailer Usually Tells the Gross Vehicle Weight Rating (GVWR)

THE RIGHT EQUIPMENT

The first step to safe transport is having the right equipment—the right trailer and right truck to tow it. One of the keys to making that match up is understanding Gross Vehicle Weight Rating (GVWR). The **GVWR** is the maximum weight of your vehicle and its load. Both your truck and your trailer will have a GVWR.

For the trailer, the GVWR is the most your trailer and its contents should weigh. (This is sometimes also called the Gross Trailer Weight Rating.) That means the weight of the trailer plus the total weight of the equipment, tools, and supplies you haul on it must not exceed the trailer's GVWR.

The trailer's GVWR should be stamped on the trailer's serial number card. If you cannot find the GVWR for your trailer, contact the trailer's manufacturer. It's important to know your trailer's GVWR. Overloading will weaken or damage your trailer and can lead to a dangerous highway incident.

To find the weight of the equipment you'll be hauling, check each machine's operator's manual. In the specifications you'll find the machine's weight. A trip to a public scale can confirm if your machine, as outfitted, weighs the same.

Remember to add in the weight of tools and supplies you'll be carrying. And make sure you recalculate the weight of the total load any time you change equipment. A new machine could mean you are overloading your trailer.

THE TOW VEHICLE

For the truck, there are two weight ratings of special concern. The first rating we'll talk about is the Gross Combined Weight Rating (GCWR). It's the maximum combined weight of the truck and trailer and all their contents. The **GCWR** should be listed in your truck's operator's manual. If you can't find the GCWR, ask your truck dealer.

To determine the gross combined weight, simply weigh your vehicle when it's fully loaded and ready to go. Add to it the weight of your loaded trailer. Check that this combined weight is lower than the GCWR for your truck. Pulling loads that put you above the GCWR could severely affect your truck's handling, braking, and performance.

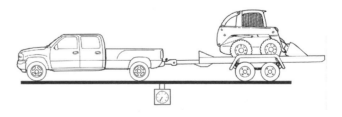

Fig. 3 – A Truck's Gross Combined Weight Rating (GCWR) Tells You the Maximum Allowable Weight of the Loaded Truck and Loaded Trailer

The other weight rating of special concern is the GVWR (Gross Vehicle Weight Rating) for your truck. Similar to the GVWR we discussed for trailers, it's the most your truck and its load should weigh. This includes the driver, passengers, and equipment or cargo carried by the truck.

Normally you would be most concerned about the weight of the cargo or equipment you have in the truck box. But when you are pulling a trailer, there's another load you must consider. It's the tongue weight of the loaded trailer.

TONGUE WEIGHT

Tongue weight is the weight of the trailer tongue pressing down on the truck's hitch. When a trailer is properly loaded, 85 to 90 percent of the weight should be carried on the trailer wheels. That leaves between 10 and 15 percent of the load carried by the trailer tongue. For example, if the weight of the trailer and load is 2,500 pounds, then the tongue weight should be between 250 and 375 pounds.

Keeping the tongue weight between 10 and 15 percent of the load is important. Too much tongue weight and you'll add stress to hitch components and take weight off the front wheels of the truck. Taking weight off the front wheels could limit steering control. Too little tongue weight and the trailer hitch may actually lift up on the rear wheels. This could affect traction.

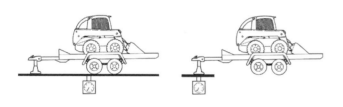

Fig. 4 – To Make Sure You Have the Proper Tongue Weight, First Load and Weigh Your Trailer. Then Place Only The Tongue on the Scale. The Tongue Should Carry Not Less Than 10 and Not More Than 15 Percent of the Total Load

You can change the tongue weight by how you load the trailer. Extra weight toward the front of the trailer will increase the tongue weight. More weight toward the rear of the trailer will decrease the tongue weight.

If you cannot get the tongue weight into the 10 to 15 percent range by rearranging the load, you may need a special weight-distributing hitch for your truck. (This type of hitch is sometimes called a load-leveling or equalizing hitch.) It distributes tongue weight to all the wheels of the towing vehicle and the trailer.

Remember, tongue weight is not only important for how it affects truck handling. It must also be added to the weight your truck is carrying when you check your truck's GVWR.

To review…

- Make sure you are not exceeding the trailer's GVWR (Gross Vehicle Weight Rating) by weighing the fully loaded trailer.

- Make sure you are not exceeding your truck's GVWR by adding the weight of the truck, the weight of all passengers and equipment on the truck, and the tongue weight.

- Make sure you are not exceeding the GCWR (gross combined weight rating) of your truck by adding the weight of your loaded trailer to the weight of your loaded truck.

- And finally, make sure the trailer's tongue weight is not less than 10 percent and not more than 15 percent of the total weight of the loaded trailer.

HITCH HEIGHT

The height of your truck hitch is also a concern. When you have your trailer hitched to the truck, the trailer floor should be level. Trailers that aren't level are more likely to bottom out and improperly transfer weight to the tow vehicle. If your trailer doesn't have this level ride, you'll need to adjust or modify either the trailer or the truck hitch.

OTHER RIGHT EQUIPMENT

Just as a chain is only as strong as its weakest link, so too the truck and trailer combination is only as strong as its weakest link. Having the right trailer hitched to an appropriate truck is not enough.

The truck's bumper hitch or frame hitch must have a rating that meets or exceeds the rating of the trailer you will pull. The hitch ball must be the same size as the trailer coupler. Using a 1 7/8-inch ball in a 2-inch coupler could allow the trailer to separate from the tow vehicle. The hitch ball itself must also have a rating that meets or exceeds the GVWR of the trailer you'll be pulling.

SAFETY CHAINS

The safety chains are another important piece of equipment. If the hitch should break or disconnect for any reason, the chains will provide an emergency connection between the truck and the trailer.

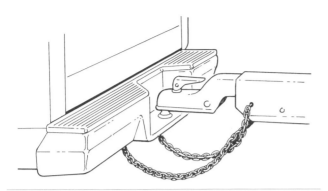

Fig. 5 – *Crossing Safety Chains Under the Trailer Hitch Makes a Cradle to Catch the Hitch if it Becomes Disconnected From the Truck*

Fig. 6 – *Surge Brakes are One Type of Trailer-braking System. When the Tow Vehicle Slows Down, the Momentum of the Trailer Pushes Against This Mechanism on the Trailer Hitch. That Pressure Engages Brakes on the Trailer's Wheels, Helping Slow the Trailer. The Cable Coming Out of the Top of the Hitch Mechanism is Connected to the Break-Away Switch*

The chains should be crossed under the tongue so they can catch and cradle a disconnected hitch. This will keep the trailer tongue from dragging or plowing into the road. The safety chains must have a rating that meets or exceeds the GVWR of the trailer.

Watch the length of safety chains. There should be enough slack so the tongue can pivot during turns, but not so much that the chains drag on the ground. Chains that drag lose their strength and should be replaced.

TRAILER BRAKES

Depending on your load, trailer brakes may be needed. Trailer brakes are brakes on the trailer's wheels that engage when the tow vehicle slows down or when you step on the tow vehicle's brakes.

There are a variety of trailer-brake systems available. Check with your trailer or truck manufacturer for the right brake system for your application. Some truck manufacturers recommend trailer brakes on any trailer with a GVWR of 1000 pounds or more. Also check your state regulations. Some states require brakes on all trailers above a certain GVWR.

A break-away switch may also be required in your state. It automatically engages the trailer's brakes system if the trailer becomes separated from the tow vehicle. Check with your trailer manufacturer or highway patrol for rules that apply in your area.

PROPER LIGHTING

Of course you'll need your trailer properly equipped with brake, turn-signal, and other lights that meet your state's rules. Before each trip, connect the trailer lights and check that they are all working. The lighting connector is susceptible to corruption. Check each time you hook up the lights that electricity flows to all functions.

DRIVE DIFFERENTLY

Even the right equipment won't prevent a mishap if you don't adjust your driving. That's because pulling a trailer, especially one loaded with equipment, will affect the handling of your truck. A loaded trailer will slow your acceleration, increase your braking distance, and limit maneuverability. In the worst of situations this could cause you to completely lose control of your truck.

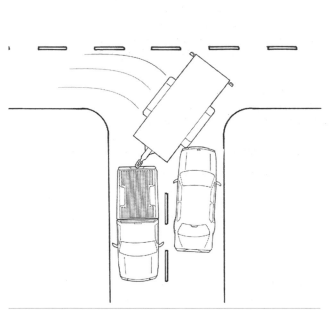

Fig. 7 – Slow Down Before You Start Your Turn. Turning Too Fast Can Cause the Trailer to "Crack the Whip" and Skid into Oncoming Traffic

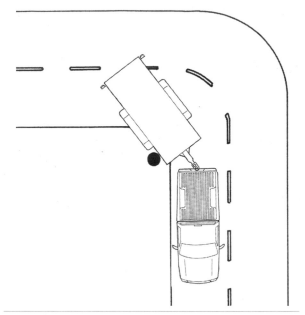

Fig. 8 – A Trailer Will Usually Make a Sharper Corner Than the Tow Vehicle. Make Wide Turns to Avoid Problems

Here are some driving tips that will help keep you incident free:

- **Slow down.** Reducing your speed gives you more time to react to traffic problems. Slower speeds are also less stressful on the equipment you are hauling.

- **Brake sooner.** Since it will take a longer distance to stop the combined weight of truck and trailer, you need to start braking earlier. Apply steady, gentle pressure to the brake pedal. Jamming on the brakes can cause the trailer to jackknife, which can throw your truck out of control.

- **Corner slowly.** If you go into a sharp corner too quickly, the trailer can skid like "crack the whip" into the other lane of traffic (Fig. 7). In some situations this force can actually pull the tow vehicle off the road. Slow down well before you come to a turn. Do your braking when the trailer and tow vehicle are in a straight line.

- **Make wide corners.** While turning, most trailers don't follow the truck tracks. Make wide turns so the trailer safely clears curbs, signs, and pedestrians on the inside of the turn (Fig. 8).

- **Practice.** Getting used to towing a trailer takes practice. Before you hit the road with the time pressures of work, practice turning and backing in a large, empty parking lot.

LOADING EQUIPMENT

How you load your trailer is also an important part of transport safety. Poorly balanced or improperly secured loads can cause real problems during transport. Plus mishaps can easily happen during the loading and unloading process.

Loading equipment is not always a big deal. Obviously, loading something like a walk-behind mower is pretty simple. But loading larger machines like skid-steer loaders or tractor backhoes pose some serious safety concerns. Check the operator's manual for specific advice on loading and tying down your machine.

Load and unload equipment only on a level surface. A sloping trailer increases the chance of equipment sliding or rolling off the trailer. Make sure the ground around the trailer is firm. Muddy or soft ground could let the trailer wheels sink and tilt the trailer. Again, this could lead to an equipment overturn.

CLEAN TRAILER
Keep trailer beds and ramps free of mud, oil, ice, snow, and other slippery materials. Slick surfaces could make it very difficult to control the equipment.

If the machine you are loading or unloading has a safety belt, wear it. Don't take chances just because you're not driving very far. Take your time and drive slowly.

Fig. 9 – Use Extreme Caution When Loading Equipment, and Always Wear Your Seatbelt

It's best to make the loading process a two-person job. With some equipment it's difficult to see the edges of the trailer from the driver's seat. Having an extra person to direct you will make the process much safer.

If you must load alone, use extreme caution. Line the machine up straight behind the trailer. Then find a floorboard or trailer edge you can sight along. Never load or unload a machine you are not familiar with. Loading and unloading some equipment is a bit like walking on a gymnastics balance beam. This is not the time to test your driving skills. One false move could have you and the equipment tumbling to the ground. If you have any doubts about your ability to do the job safely, don't do it. Find a helper to direct you, or find a more experienced driver.

This Could Be You...Laurie couldn't believe she got stuck with this job. Sure she liked to drive the skid steer, but she hadn't done it all that often. And she had never driven it with this much snow on the ground. But Jose said he needed it loaded onto the trailer, and she was the only one in the office. He assured her she could do it, no problem. Things were going OK until she was halfway up the trailer ramp. The tires started to slip on the snow. Maybe she needed a running start. This would be tricky because it was hard to distinguish the snow-covered trailer from the snow-covered ground. But she knew she could do it. It was an hour later that Jose drove into the yard and saw the skid steer lying on its side next to the trailer. "Oh my God," he thought, "what have I done."

As we discussed in the section about tongue weight, how you position equipment on the trailer is important. The load must be evenly balanced on the trailer right to left and front to rear. Too much weight on one side of the trailer increases the chance of an overturn or other mishap. Too much weight front or rear will affect tongue weight.

TYING DOWN EQUIPMENT

Once the machine is safely on the trailer, lower all implements and attachments, set the brakes, and remove the key. Leaving the key in the ignition only increases the chance of theft and vandalism.

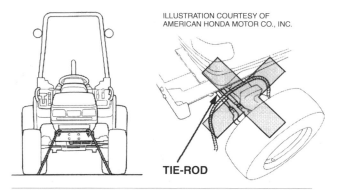

ILLUSTRATION COURTESY OF AMERICAN HONDA MOTOR CO., INC.

TIE-ROD

Fig. 10 – Securely Tie All Equipment to the Trailer. With Larger Machines, Tie Down Both the Front and Rear With Straps Going Downward and Outward. Never Put Straps or Chains Over Steering Cylinders or Steering Tie Rods

Tie down the machine using heavy-duty straps or chains. Secure the front and rear of the machine, tying straps downward and outward. Tighten these tie downs so equipment is held firmly in place and can't rub against trailer parts or other equipment.

Check the machine's operator's manual for advice on tie-down points. The tie-down points you use must be strong and solid. Never put straps or chains over steering cylinders or steering tie rods. This can damage the machine, plus these points are not strong enough to fully secure the equipment to the trailer.

It's very important that all items on the trailer, both large and small, are securely tied or attached to the trailer. Losing tools or equipment at highway speeds can cause serious injuries to others on the road.

OTHER SAFETY CONCERNS

Passengers. Never allow passengers on the trailer being towed. It is dangerous and against the law in most areas.

Check tire pressure. Make sure all trailer and truck tires have the recommended air pressure. Big loads cause rapid wear on under-inflated tires.

Lubricate hitch ball. A dry coupler and hitch ball will cause excessive wear. When not in use, cover the hitch ball to prevent rust buildup.

Secure coupler lever. Pin or padlock the latching lever on the hitch coupler. If not secured, the latch could open and disconnect from the truck.

Do trailer maintenance. Keep your trailer in top condition. Grease wheel bearings, especially if the trailer has been idle for several months. Condensation can build up in idle bearings. Replace any rotted or damaged floorboards.

Cover SMV. If equipment on the trailer has an SMV (slow moving vehicle) emblem, remove or cover it. Other motorists, seeing an SMV, will think you are going less than 25 mph.

FUEL TRANSPORT

Most people would recognize that gasoline poses a potential hazard. But did you know one gallon of gasoline has the explosive power of more than 80 pounds of dynamite? It's pretty obvious that fuels, especially gasoline, should be handled with great care.

Carry gasoline and diesel fuel in only approved safety containers. These cans should be made of heavy gauge metal. Make sure it's easy to tell gasoline from diesel fuel. Use approved red containers to hold gasoline and approved yellow or green containers to hold diesel. Don't run the risk of someone confusing gasoline for diesel fuel and damaging an engine.

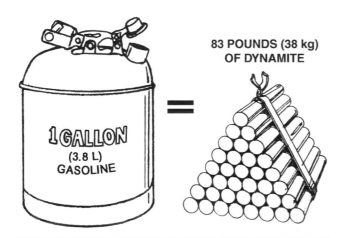

83 POUNDS (38 kg) OF DYNAMITE

Fig. 11 – One Gallon of Gasoline Can Have the Explosive Force of 83 Pounds of Dynamite

Never carry fuel in leftover glass or plastic containers. The shape and color of these recycled containers will hide the fact that they contain flammable, explosive fuels. Plus, some container materials actually disintegrate with long-term exposure to gasoline or diesel fuel.

When filling a fuel container, place it flatly on the ground. Never fill a fuel container while it's sitting in a pickup truck, especially if there is a plastic bed liner. Numerous truck fires have resulted from fuel spilled on plastic bed liners. These liners can generate static electricity that will produce fire-starting sparks.

Before you drive anywhere, make sure all fuel-container caps and vent-hole covers are closed tight. Anchor the containers to the trailer or truck bed. This could be as simple as running a rope across the trailer that runs through all the fuel container handles.

REFUELING

Use care when refueling on the job. Let hot engines cool at least five minutes before refueling. Waiting longer is even better. If you spill fuel, wait for it to evaporate before starting the engine.

Keep flames and sparks away from fuel and fumes. Before refueling, properly dispose of cigarettes and turn off the engine and all electrical switches. Remember gasoline fumes are heavier than air, so they sink. A hot engine or a discarded cigarette could cause an explosion. Always refuel outdoors.

ADDITIONAL RESOURCES
The National Ag Safety Database http://www.cdc.gov/niosh/nasd/nasdhome.html. Check the video "Professional's Guide to Lawn Mower Safety".

TEST YOURSELF

QUESTIONS - CHAPTER 15

1. List the four main causes of equipment-transport mishaps.

2. What does GVWR mean?

3. What must you do to know a trailer full of equipment does not exceed your truck's GVWR?

4. What is tongue weight and how can it affect your truck's handling?

5. Why are trailer brakes important?

6. Why is it generally best to have two people when loading large equipment?

7. Name four ways you should drive differently when pulling a trailer.

SAFETY IN THE MAINTENANCE SHOP

INTRODUCTION

One ingredient of working safely with outdoor power equipment is a well-equipped and well-managed shop. That's because a good shop helps keep equipment well maintained; well-maintained equipment works better; equipment that works better helps prevent operator frustration and the operator who's not frustrated will be a safer operator.

Well-maintained equipment is also more likely to have all its shielding in place and other safety equipment in good repair. That, too, helps prevent injuries.

But a shop has its own potential dangers. In this chapter we'll look at some important safety issues in the maintenance shop and give you some tips that will help keep your shop incident free.

IMPORTANT SAFETY CONCERNS

Shops vary greatly from business to business and therefore so do the potential hazards. For users of landscape and golf course equipment, here are some of the typical shop-related safety issues:

- **Eye injuries**
- **Crushing injuries**
- **Electric shock**
- **Grinder injuries**
- **Carbon monoxide**
- **Falls**
- **Battery acid and explosions.**

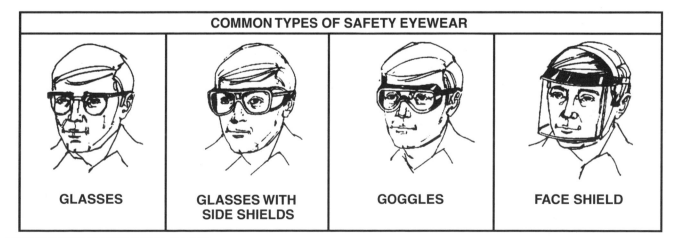

Fig. 1 – Common Types of Safety Eyewear

Let's look at each of these safety issues and discuss ways to make your shop a safer place to work.

EYE INJURIES

There are many ways eyes can get injured in the shop—flying metal from chisels or other hand tools, metal chips from grinders, and chemical burns from solvents or lubricants. An important line of defense for all of these injuries is proper eye protection.

There is a wide variety of safety glasses that can protect your eyes. If you wear eyeglasses for work, make sure they are approved safety glasses. Safety glasses are made with special impact-resistant materials so they withstand more shock than ordinary lenses. Side shields should be added to the glasses to guard against flying particles coming from the side. There are also safety glasses designed to be worn over your prescription glasses. Eye protection that resists impact is marked with the ANSI Z87.1 coding.

Goggles protect the eyes from impact from the front and sides. Some goggles have vents to limit perspiration buildup and fogging of the lenses. Unvented goggles provide protection against chemical vapors and liquids.

Face shields protect the face from splashing, dust, and chaff, but they provide very little protection against impact. If there is the chance of flying objects when and where you use a face shield, wear safety glasses or goggles under the shield.

What is an ANSI code?
ANSI stands for the American National Standards Institute. It is a non-profit, membership organization that helps develop design and performance standards for a wide variety of businesses and technologies. These standards are much like rules that manufacturers agree to follow. With eye protection, for example, if a pair of safety glasses meets the ANSI standard, you know it is made of special impact-resistant materials that can withstand a high level of shock. If you buy eye protection that doesn't meet the ANSI standard, you can't be sure how much protection you really have.

PUT THEM ON

It's important that everyone in the shop wear proper eye protection at all times. You can never tell when or where bits of debris will fly. But getting everyone to wear eye protection is often easier said than done. Here are some ways you can help make it happen:

- Discuss the danger of eye injuries and the importance of safety glasses with employees

- Make wearing safety glasses mandatory for all visitors and employees in the shop

- Have a supply of safety glasses in a covered, dust-proof box at all entrances to the shop. That way it's easy for everyone to put on clean glasses before they enter the shop

- Post the safety rules at shop entrances and enforce them with everyone

- Keep a supply of brand-new safety glasses on hand. People will not use glasses that are scratched or stained.

While safety glasses are an important defense against eye injuries, it's also important to work on prevention. That means being on the lookout for items or situations that could cause eye injuries.

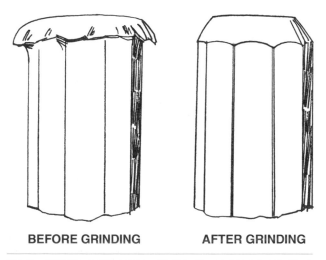

BEFORE GRINDING   **AFTER GRINDING**

Fig. 2 – Chisels and Punches with "Mushroom" Heads are More Likely to Cause Eye Injuries. Grind Off the Mushroomed Metal Before it Flies Off From a Hammer Blow

Repair or replace worn or damaged tools that could cause eye injuries. For example, older chisels and punches can develop "mushroom" heads. Pounding on a mushroom head can cause bits of metal to go flying and cause eye injuries. You can help prevent this by grinding off the mushroomed metal.

Use the right tools for the job. A screwdriver that's being used as a pry bar is more likely to break. Using a wrench as a hammer can damage the wrench and send wrench bits into the air.

Also keep all shields in place. On a grinder, for example, the eye shields provide an extra level of protection from flying bits of metal and abrasives.

This Could Be You...This time around, the holes on the bracket just wouldn't line up. The rest of the repair had gone well, and now this. Al picked up a screwdriver and tried pushing the bracket over. Then he took a hammer and tried to tap the bracket over. Then he tried prying with the screwdriver. Finally he took the hammer and using the screwdriver like a punch started pounding on the screwdriver handle. It was at the third pound when Al felt a shooting pain in his left eye. He instinctively reached up and rubbed. Suddenly it felt as if a red-hot poker were in his eye.

CRUSHING INJURIES

To properly perform some repairs, equipment needs to be raised off the ground. But by raising equipment you greatly increase the risk of a serious crushing injury. That's why it's very important to follow safety rules when using a jack.

Before you jack up any equipment, make sure the machine is on firm, level ground. Engage the brakes and block the wheels so the machine doesn't move.

Be sure the jack is strong enough to raise the machine. Check the rated capacity of the jack against the weight of the machine. With an overloaded jack, there is the danger of sudden failure.

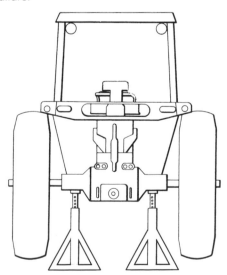

Fig. 3 – Once Equipment is Jacked to the Desired Height, Support the Machine With Stands and Remove the Jack

Lift no higher than necessary and immediately support the machine with stands or large wooden blocks. Never allow raised equipment to remain supported by jacks alone. If the jack would fail or tip, your machine could fall unexpectedly, resulting in a severe crushing injury.

ELECTRIC SHOCK

To understand the potential hazard of electricity, we'll need to cover a few electricity basics. Let's look at a basic electrical outlet. The right-hand slot is called the "hot" side of the outlet because that is where the electrical current originates. The left-hand slot is called the "neutral" side of the outlet. When you plug in a light, for example, electricity flows from the hot side of the outlet, through the light bulb, and then back into the neutral side of the outlet.

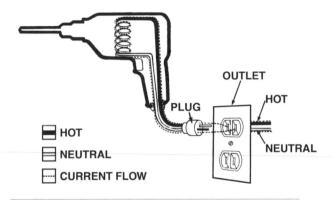

Fig. 4 – With a Properly Operating Tool, All Electricity Moves From the Hot Side of the Outlet Through the Tool and Back Out the Neutral Side of the Outlet

Plug in a tool—an electric drill for example—and a similar thing happens. When you pull the trigger on the drill, the electricity flows from the hot side of the outlet, up the electrical cord, through the tool, down the cord, and back out the neutral side of the outlet. This flow of electricity makes the drill turn.

If the insulation around the cord and in the drill is in perfect condition, all current entering the drill from the hot side of the outlet will exit through the neutral side of the outlet. But, if the insulation on the cord is cracked, or the insulation inside the drill is faulty, some of that current may try to "leak" out and give the drill operator a shock. Depending on how badly the insulation is cracked, you may feel anything from a slight tingle to a life-threatening jolt.

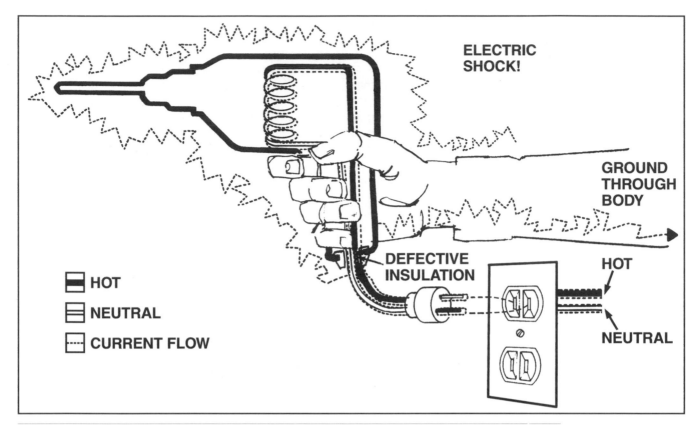

ELECTRIC SHOCK!

GROUND THROUGH BODY

DEFECTIVE INSULATION

HOT

NEUTRAL

▬ HOT

▤ NEUTRAL

┅ CURRENT FLOW

Fig. 5 – If the Insulation on the Tool is Cracked or Defective, Some of the Electricity May Leak Out to the Operator

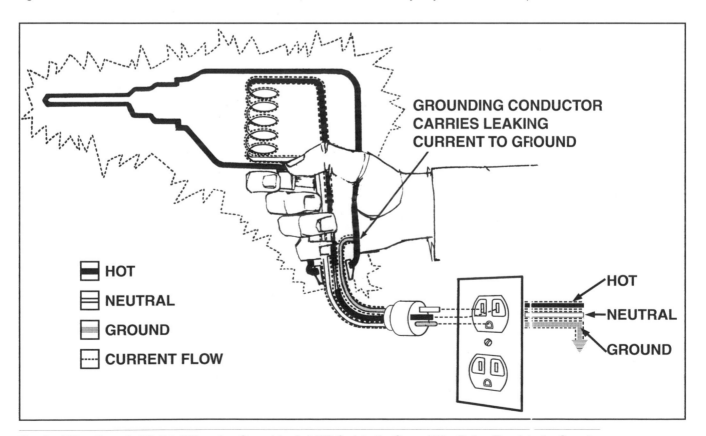

GROUNDING CONDUCTOR CARRIES LEAKING CURRENT TO GROUND

HOT

NEUTRAL

GROUND

▬ HOT

▤ NEUTRAL

▦ GROUND

┅ CURRENT FLOW

Fig. 6 – With a Grounded Outlet, if There is a Current Leak, it Will Go into the Ground Wire Rather Than into the Operator

That's because electricity is always looking for a ground. That ground can be the neutral side of the electrical outlet, or that ground could be through the operator. The electricity really doesn't care how it finds a ground. It just takes the easiest path. Now the bad news. Skin, especially skin wet with perspiration, is a conductor of electricity. That's why you need to take steps to make sure no electrical power reaches the operator.

GROUNDED OUTLETS

One of those steps is to have only grounded outlets in your shop. Grounded outlets have a third, round hole. This third hole is called a grounding conductor, or typically just a "ground." Put a 3-prong plug into a grounded outlet and your tool has an extra level of shock protection.

The ground normally carries no electricity. It's there just in case the electricity needs a place to flow during some kind of malfunction. Let's say there's a loose wire in the tool, and this loose wire could transmit electricity out to the operator. The ground wire gives this electricity an easier place to go. Since electricity always takes the easiest path, it will run down the grounded wire and into the grounded outlet rather than into the operator. While damp skin is a conductor of electricity, the grounded copper wire is a much better conductor.

What happens if someone has snipped off the third prong of the plug? Without the third prong on the plug, there's no protection. Leaking electricity can't make it to the grounded outlet, so it will go through the operator. That's why you should never remove the third prong of a plug. With no connection, there's no protection.

Now you can't assume all three-hole outlets are grounded. Anyone can put a grounded outlet into an ungrounded electrical box. If there isn't a ground connection in the wiring behind the outlet, you won't have shock protection. Fortunately, it is easy to tell if a circuit is grounded. It can be done with a simple current tester. If you're not sure which outlets are actually grounded, have a qualified person check.

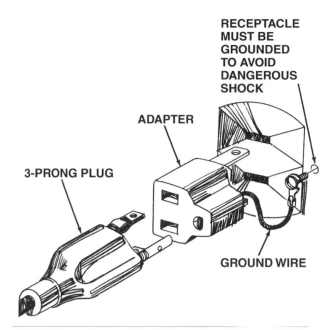

RECEPTACLE MUST BE GROUNDED TO AVOID DANGEROUS SHOCK

ADAPTER

3-PRONG PLUG

GROUND WIRE

Fig. 7 – Adapters Do Not Necessarily Give You any Grounding Protection. If the Circuit or Outlet Box isn't Grounded, the Tool's Third Prong Can't Carry any Electrical Leaks

What do you do if you have a tool with a 3-prong plug, but your outlet has only two holes? The correct answer is to call an electrician and get that outlet grounded. Don't think an adapter will necessarily give you protection. If the circuit itself isn't grounded, an adapter won't provide a ground. Again, no connection, no protection.

DOUBLE-INSULATED TOOLS

Because many homes and garages don't have grounded outlets, some power tools are manufactured with double layers of insulation. If one layer becomes defective, a second layer provides protection from shock.

Tools with double insulation can be safely used in "2-prong" outlets since the double insulation provides an extra level of shock protection. These tools are identified by the words "Double Insulation" or a symbol that shows a small square within a larger square. Double-insulated tools frequently have a plastic outer covering.

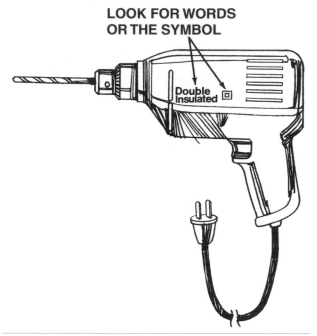

LOOK FOR WORDS OR THE SYMBOL

Double Insulated

Fig. 8 – Double-Insulated Tools are Clearly Marked on the Case or Nameplate

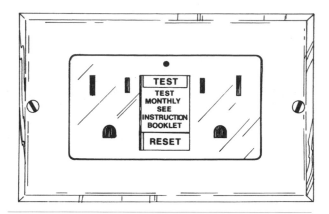

TEST

TEST MONTHLY SEE INSTRUCTION BOOKLET

RESET

Fig. 9 – A Ground-Fault Interrupter Outlet Senses the Electricity Flow and Kicks Out if There is an Electrical Leak

Ground-fault interrupters are required by many building codes for outdoor outlets and outlets near sources of water. But regardless of your local building code, GFI protection is a great idea for a shop and anywhere else electricity is used in damp situations. If you have a GFI outlet or a GFI circuit breaker, follow directions and test the circuit regularly.

GOOD MAINTENANCE

Don't think properly protected electrical circuits mean you can ignore tool maintenance. Make sure all electrical cords are in excellent condition. Small cracks in cords should be promptly repaired with electrical tape. If cords have larger cracks that expose the internal insulation, they should be replaced immediately.

Also watch for damage on the power tool itself. Any time a tool has a cracked housing or sounds or smells unusual, it should be discarded or taken in for repair. Don't take chances. A damaged tool can lead electricity to you.

These tools do provide good shock protection if conditions are dry. But there is a danger of electrical shock if you are working in damp conditions. Three-wire grounded tools provide almost complete protection and are highly recommended.

GROUND-FAULT INTERRUPTER

While the grounded outlet does provide a high level of protection, there is something better—the ground-fault interrupter (GFI). A GFI comes in the form of an outlet or a GFI circuit breaker. A GFI has circuitry that senses how much electricity flows out of the hot side of an outlet and how much flows back into the neutral side.

Earlier we said all the electricity should flow from the hot side of the outlet, through the tool, and then back into the neutral side of the outlet. If more electricity flows in from the hot side than flows out the neutral side, what's missing is probably giving someone a shock.

Whenever a GFI senses a difference between the current going out and the current coming in, it immediately kicks out and shuts off the power flow. As little as .005 of an amp difference will kick out the GFI. It happens so fast, the circuit shuts down before you can get a serious shock.

For example, say you have a crack in an extension cord. If electricity leaks out that crack onto wet grass, the GFI will kick out. Or if you use a power washer and the spray gets on an electrical connection, the GFI will kick out before you can get a shock.

STATIONARY GRINDERS

A stationary grinder makes quick work of sharpening a mower blade or removing mushroomed metal from a chisel or punch. But because they are so aggressive they pose some special safety concerns. These include possible injuries from flying debris, entangled hair or clothing, and abrasions from the grinding wheel.

An important first step to protect yourself from flying debris is to have all shields in place. The eye shield and the wheel shield will help contain bits of metal and sand that fly off during grinding. These shields also help contain chunks of the grinding wheel if it should break or shatter at high speed.

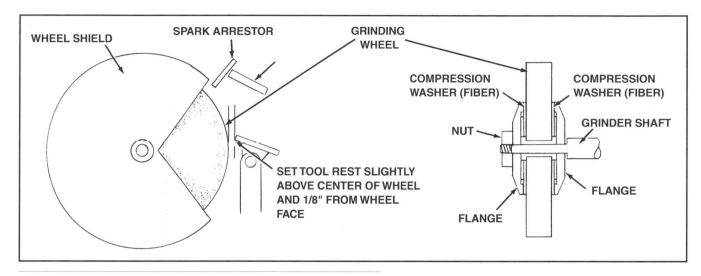

Fig. 10 – Keep All Grinder Shields in Place and Always Wear Safety Glasses

Because grinders spit out sparks and bits of flying metal, always wear safety glasses when using a grinder. Protect your eyes even if your grinder has a shatter-proof eye shield.

Sturdy gloves are also important. They offer protection from sparks and from the abrasives on the wheel. Try to keep your hands as far away as possible from the spinning grinding wheel. Remember, if the grinder can take off metal, it will quickly go through gloves and flesh.

If you are grinding a relatively small object, grip it with a pliers or locking wrench. This will move your hand farther away from the wheel. Plus the pliers will protect your fingers from burns as your work object heats up. Use moderate pressure and grind only on the face of the wheel. Side pressures may break the wheel unless it is specifically designed for side-pressure grinding.

To further protect your hands, never adjust the grinder while the grinding wheel is still turning. Turn off the power and wait until the wheel has come to a complete stop before moving the tool rest or making other adjustments.

ENTANGLEMENTS

Entanglements are also a potential problem with grinders. The grinding wheel turns at a high speed. If it should catch some hair or a dangling thread it could pull you into the spinning wheel.

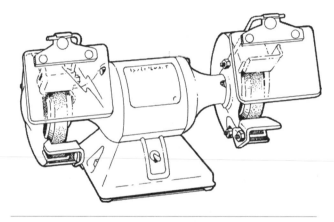

Fig. 11 – Use Extreme Caution If Your Grinder Has a Wire Brush Wheel. It Will Aggressively Grab Clothing or Hair, Resulting in an Entanglement Injury

Of even more concern is the round wire brushes used on some grinders.

These are great for cleaning rust and dirt from objects, but the wire bristles will aggressively grab anything that gets in its path. If a spinning wire brush should latch on to some of your hair or a scarf or jewelry you are in for a serious injury.

Never use a grinder if you have anything loose hanging down from your face, neck, or arm. Tie up hair securely and stuff it into a cap. Remove any dangly jewelry and check your clothing for rips or loose threads. Any of these items could get grabbed by a grinding wheel or wire brush wheel.

Even though grinding wheels are tough, they are also brittle and thus easy to break if dropped or misused. Grinders turn at high speed and a crack in the wheel can cause it to break up sending pieces to fly in all directions. Even a brand new abrasive wheel can have a crack, so give it the "ring test" before you install it. Hold up the wheel on one finger and then gently tap the wheel with a light metal object. A clear "ring" indicates a good wheel. No "ring" means the wheel is defective and should be replaced.

Make sure the speed of your grinder doesn't exceed the recommended speed for the new wheel. The grinder speed should be displayed on the motor nameplate. The maximum recommended speed for the abrasive wheel is on its label.

CARBON MONOXIDE

Of all the fumes that can build up in a shop, none is more sneaky or dangerous than carbon monoxide (CO). It's a colorless, odorless gas that is present in the exhaust of all outdoor power equipment.

CO blocks the normal movement of oxygen into the blood. Breathing air contaminated with CO literally starves your body of oxygen, resulting in coma and death.

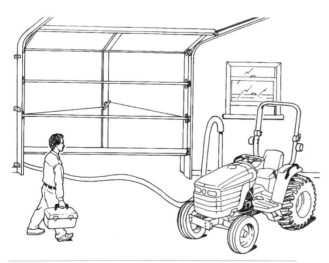

Fig. 12 – If You Must Run an Engine Inside the Shop, Use an Exhaust Pipe Extension to Vent Fumes Outdoors. Also Open Doors and Windows So There is Fresh Air Coming into the Shop

The danger of carbon monoxide is not just that it is deadly, but that its buildup typically goes unnoticed. If an engine is run in a closed area, workers can be overcome and pass out before they realize they are in any danger.

The best rule is to never run an engine in an enclosed area. If you must run an engine indoors, use an exhaust pipe extension to vent fumes outside (Fig.12). Even when using an exhaust pipe extension, make sure there is fresh air coming into the building.

Engines are not the only source of CO. Other sources include malfunctioning furnaces or shop heaters, as well as charcoal grills. Since these other sources can also give off CO, you can get an added level of protection by installing a CO detector. A CO detector will sound an alarm, much like a smoke detector, when dangerous levels of CO are in the atmosphere.

For the shop environment buy a top quality CO detector. Models that give a digital readout of the CO level are less troubled by dirt and dust and can be reset after they go off.

However, don't think installing a CO detector means you can ignore safety rules. Never run an engine in a closed shop, thinking the detector will keep you safe. The best way to stay safe from the danger of CO is to vent exhaust fumes outdoors.

FALLS

Many people are surprised to learn that falls are a major cause of work-related injuries in the United States. National Safety Council statistics show that more than 300,000 people are injured each year by falling on the job.

You can do a lot to prevent falls in your shop by paying attention to:

- **Good footing**
- **Good lighting and**
- **Good housekeeping.**

GOOD FOOTING

Many falls result from slippery floors. You can take steps to prevent this. Clean up any oil spills immediately. Have sand, or a similar commercial product, on hand to add traction to slippery areas.

It's not uncommon for shop floors to become cracked, pitted, or uneven. It pays to fix these imperfections before someone trips and is injured. Repairing a shop floor is not cheap, but it may well be less than one trip to the emergency room.

Develop a system of racks, bins, or tool boards so finding the right tool or supply is easy and quick. Never store tools or spare parts in alley-ways or on the work floor where someone could trip over them.

Take special care when storing flammable or hazardous materials. Grease, oil, paint, and solvents should be stored in metal cabinets or on metal shelves. Wooden shelves can get soaked and absorb these flammable materials, creating a fire hazard.

Fig. 13 – Good Lighting in Alley-Ways and Storage Areas Helps Limit Falls. If You Have Raised a Storage Area, Make Sure it is Protected By a Railing

If your shop has stairs or a raised storage area, make sure they are protected by strong railings. Railings will prevent falls and are required by occupational safety regulations.

GOOD LIGHTING

Proper lighting not only makes a shop safer, it can make employees more efficient. Adding workstation lights will make it easier and safer to do repairs on the workbench. Better mobile lights will improve repairs done out on the shop floor. And adding light to dark corners and storage areas will help prevent tripping and other falls.

You can also brighten your shop by painting the walls and ceiling a light color. A fresh coat of light paint will make your shop look larger and brighten dark corners and alley-ways.

GOOD HOUSEKEEPING

A clean shop is a safer shop. Tripping injuries will be prevented if tools and supplies are properly stored and walk ways kept clean. Make it standard procedure in your shop that all tools and supplies are put away at the end of each day, and at the end of each job.

Fig. 14 – Store Oily Rags in a Metal Container with a Self-Closing Lid

Use steel drums for collecting trash. Use one drum for combustibles like paper and cardboard and a separate drum for non-combustibles like metals. Also provide a metal container with a self-closing cover for oily shop rags. The self-closing cover keeps sparks and hot metal from accidentally reaching the used rags. Plus the cover limits the air that would feed any fire that did ignite in the can.

Be sure to empty all trash and rag containers frequently. Limiting the trash that's in your shop will limit the chance of falls and fire. Consult your area's recycling office for advice on recycling or disposing of motor oil, oil filters, antifreeze, and other hazardous wastes.

This Could Be You...It was just a quick tire change, so Evan didn't see any reason to drag out the stands. He had a new tire on a new rim, and the whole job would only take a minute. So he'd jacked up the tractor with the hydraulic jack and started loosening the lug nuts. They came off easier than he thought. Evan had already placed the new rim on the axle when his foot bumped the pile of lug nuts. They went rolling in all directions. One went under the tractor, right next to the jack. Evan bent down and reached under the tractor to get it. Now, half lying under the tractor, Evan had his head close to the jack. That was the only reason he heard the woosh of oil as a seal in the jack broke. The tractor dropped 5 inches in an instant. That's when the rim caught on the threads of the lug bolts. A few bits of metal had saved Evan from being crushed.

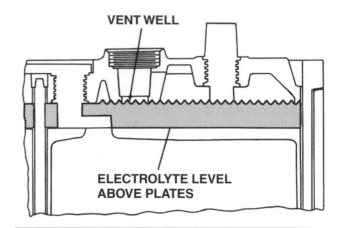

Fig. 15 – Keeping Fluids at the Proper Level Inside the Battery Reduces the Volume of Accumulated Hydrogen Gas

BATTERY SAFETY

The liquid inside lead-acid batteries contains sulfuric acid. Even though it's diluted, the acid is strong enough to burn skin, eat holes in clothing, and cause blindness if splashed into eyes.

Always wear eye protection when working around batteries and battery fluid. If you do spill acid on yourself, flush your skin immediately with lots of water. Continue flushing for several minutes. Apply baking soda or lime to help neutralize the acid.

If acid gets into your eyes, force the lids open and flood the eyes with running water for 15 to 30 minutes. Get to a doctor at once.

BATTERY EXPLOSIONS

A battery explosion is caused by a buildup of hydrogen gas. Hydrogen is given off whenever lead-acid batteries are charged. When mixed with the oxygen in the air, hydrogen is highly explosive. If the concentration of hydrogen is high enough, any spark or flame near the battery could ignite these gases, rupturing the battery case, and throwing acid in all directions.

To prevent battery explosions, you can do two things. Limit the buildup of hydrogen gas and limit any sparks near the battery.

You can limit hydrogen buildup by keeping battery "water" at the recommended level. If cells have the proper amount of fluid, there's less space in the battery for gases to accumulate.

There are many ways to limit sparks near a battery. Use a flashlight to check electrolyte level. A match or lighter could set off an explosion. Never smoke when working around batteries.

A battery charger can also cause potentially dangerous sparks. Turn the battery charger off, or pull the power cord, before connecting or disconnecting charger clamps to the battery. If your battery charger current is turned on, a spark will jump between the charger clamp and the battery. Any spark could ignite the hydrogen gas that is always present when a battery is being charged.

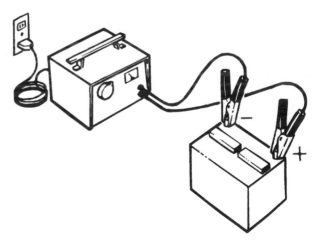

Fig. 16 – To Prevent a Spark, Turn Off or Unplug the Battery Charger Before Removing Clamps from the Battery Posts

You can also reduce sparking by removing and replacing a machine's battery connections in the proper order. That means the grounded clamp should be removed first and reconnected last. Why is this important? When a machine's battery is connected, all parts of the engine and frame are tied to the negative terminal. If your wrench is on the positive battery terminal and it touches the machine chassis, a heavy flow of current will produce a dangerous spark. If you remove the ground clamp first (and replace it last), there will be no spark.

CHARGING MANY BATTERIES

With a single battery, the danger comes from a buildup of hydrogen gas inside the battery. But if you are charging banks of batteries, such as in a shed full of electric utility vehicles, dangerous amounts of hydrogen gas can build up in the building. Here there is the danger of a huge explosion.

That's why electric utility vehicles should be recharged only in a well-ventilated area. Industry standards recommend five air changes per hour.

NEED A JUMP?

Jumping a battery typically means using the good battery in one vehicle to start the engine on a vehicle that has a weak or drained battery. Once the "dead" engine has started, it can generally recharge its own battery.

Even though this procedure is done thousands of times each day without problems, it can be dangerous. You can prevent battery explosions and other serious incidents by following these steps. Check your machine's operator's manual for other tips.

- Remove caps on battery cells (if so equipped)
- Check for ice in the cells. Never attempt to jumpstart a battery with frozen cells. Warm the battery to 60F (16 C)
- Add battery water if low; replace caps
- Be sure that the dead battery and the good battery are the same voltage
- Turn off ignition and accessories on both vehicles
- Put both vehicles in neutral or park and set the parking brake.
- Attach one red clamp of the jumper cables to the positive terminal of the good battery

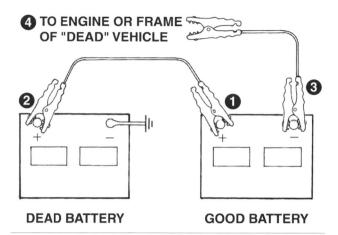

Fig. 17 – Attach Battery Clamps in the Proper Order—1. Positive Terminal of Good Battery 2. Positive Terminal of the Dead Battery 3. Negative Terminal of the Good Battery 4. Engine Ground Somewhere Below the Dead Battery. Remove Clamps in Reverse Order

- Attach the other red clamp to the positive post of dead battery
- Attach one black clamp to the negative post of the good battery
- Connect the other black clamp to the engine block or vehicle frame of the "dead" vehicle. Attach this last clamp below and away from the dead battery. This last clamp completes the circuit and will cause a spark. Since hydrogen is lighter than air, a low connection will put that spark away from any hydrogen gas
- When you remove the cables, do it in reverse order—first the black clamp from the engine block, then the black clamp from the negative post on the good battery, then the red clamp on the dead battery, and lastly, remove the red clamp from the positive post of the good battery.
- While jumping, never run the starter for more than 30 seconds because it may overheat and fail. If the vehicle with the dead battery will not start, start the other vehicle and let it run for several minutes with the cables attached. Then try it again. This will help charge up the dead battery.
- To prevent sparks and possible battery explosion, never allow clamps on one end of the jumper cables to touch while the other end is attached to a battery.

RECYCLE YOUR BATTERIES

Lead-acid batteries, along with the rechargeable nickel-cadmium batteries found on some outdoor power equipment, pose special environmental risks.

Lead-acid batteries contain lead, along with sulfuric acid, and are considered a hazardous material. In most areas it is against the law to put these batteries into the trash. Fortunately, they are easy to recycle at most automobile service shops and battery retailers.

Nickel-cadmium (Ni-Cad) batteries also contain heavy metals and are considered hazardous waste. These batteries are usually found on rechargeable hand tools, and rechargeable yard tools. Never throw these batteries in the trash. They should not go into landfills or incinerators. To find the nearest place to recycle them, call 1-800-8-BATTERY.

SHOP CHECKLIST

Here's a list of equipment to have and management steps to take. Put these tools and ideas to work and you'll have a safer shop.

- Fire extinguishers. Have two in your shop, one for chemical fires and one for other combustible fires. See Chapter 4 for more fire extinguisher information.

- Have smoke alarms and a carbon monoxide monitor. Test regularly and replace batteries on schedule.

- Have an industrial-quality first aid kit in a prominent location. The kit should include eye wash, sterilizing pads or solutions, antibiotic ointment, assorted bandages, tweezers and magnifying lens, and single-use cold packs. Check and replenish supplies regularly.

- Keep a file box for operator's manuals and safety instructions that come with shop tools and equipment.

- Allow no one to use tools or equipment unless they've had adequate instruction.

- Use tools for the jobs they were designed to do. Wrenches are not hammers. Screwdrivers are not chisels.

- Keep guards and other safety devices in place and functioning.

- Issue safety glasses to all employees and keep a supply handy for visitors.

- Stock various kinds of gloves to protect hands from solvents and sharp tools. See Chapter 2 for more information on gloves.

- Use proper solvents for cleaning parts. Never use gasoline or diesel fuel. Skin exposure to diesel fuel is a suspected cause of cancer, and gasoline poses an extreme risk of explosion.

- Have proper hearing protection available for noisy shop operations. See Chapter 2 for more information.

- Wear sturdy leather work boots, preferably with steel toes.

- Keep toxic solutions in a padlocked cabinet.

- Have a telephone in the shop. Program in numbers for emergency contacts and a nearby business or neighbor in case you need to call for help. Remember portable phones will not work during a power outage so have available a cellular phone or one simple plug-in phone.

- Keep all tools and service equipment in good condition.

- Keep floors clean of trash and spills to reduce fire and tripping hazards.

- Empty trash containers regularly.

ADDITIONAL RESOURCES

Employee Safety, and information packet compiled by Golf Course Superintendents Association of America, 1421 Research Park Dr., Lawrence KS 66049; 800-472-7878.

National Institute for Occupational Safety and Health website: http://www.cdc.gov/niosh/homepage.html. Check out items on shop safety and videos on proper tool and grinder use.

TEST YOURSELF

QUESTIONS - CHAPTER 16

1. Why should eye protection always be worn in a shop?

2. How does a GFI circuit protect a person using an electric tool?

3. Why should you never use a jack to hold up equipment during repairs?

4. Why is a wire brush wheel on a stationary grinder a special hazard?

5. List three things that can help prevent slips and falls.

6. If you must run an engine indoors, what must you do to prevent carbon monoxide poisoning?

7. List three things you can do to prevent a battery explosion.

GLOSSARY

A

ANSI

ANSI stands for the American National Standards Institute. It is a non-profit, membership organization that helps develop design and performance standards for a wide variety of businesses and technologies. Safety equipment that meets an ANSI standard is your assurance of a certain level of performance.

B

BALLAST

Weight added to a tractor or other machine to increase traction and stability. Typically the weight is cast iron that is attached to the front or rear of a machine.

BASE OF STABILITY

The base on which an object stands. A tractor's base of stability is the length and width between its wheels.

C

CARBON MONOXIDE (CO)

A colorless and odorless gas found in the exhaust of gasoline and diesel engines. It is very dangerous because it limits the normal movement of oxygen into the blood stream. Breathing air contaminated with CO literally starves your body of oxygen, resulting in coma and death.

CENTER OF GRAVITY

The point about which all parts of an object exactly balance one another. When considering a machine's tendency to tip over, it is as if all of the machine's weight is concentrated in one point, that being the center of gravity.

COMPACT TRACTOR

In industry there is no exact definition for a compact tractor. For this book we consider compact tractors to be those with 40 horsepower or less. Compact tractors are the most common used by landscapers, golf courses, and grounds-care professionals.

CONSULTATION PROGRAM

A state-run program, largely funded by OSHA, to help employers find out about potential workplace hazards and to assist them in improving their safety and health management. The service is free and voluntary. Check out "consultation services" on the OSHA website www.osha.gov.

D

DANGER ZONE

This is an area surrounding a power tool where the risk of injury from a thrown object is the greatest. The operator and any needed helper in the danger zone must wear all the recommended protective gear.

DIRECT COSTS

These are the medical expenses and lost wages that result from a workplace injury or mishap. Since the direct costs are most visible and easiest to add up, they are sometimes the only costs an employer considers. See indirect costs.

DRAWBAR

The place where wagons and implements are attached at the rear of a tractor.

DRIFT

The windblown movement of a pesticide onto an area where it is not supposed to be.

E

EXHAUST PIPE EXTENSION

A pipe used to send exhaust gasses out of doors. It keeps carbon monoxide from building up inside a shop or other closed area. See the illustration, Chapter 16 (Fig. 12).

F

FERTILIZER

Material used to make soil more fertile, thus improving plant growth.

G

GCWR (GROSS COMBINED WEIGHT RATING)
The maximum weight a truck or other tow vehicle can safely handle. To calculate the gross combined weight of truck and trailer, you add up the weight of the truck and the trailer and all their contents. To operate safely, this combined weight must be less than the truck's CGWR.

GVWR (GROSS VEHICLE WEIGHT RATING)
The maximum allowable weight of a vehicle and its load. Both trucks and trailers will have a GVWR. Sometimes a trailer's rating is called a Gross Trailer Weight Rating.

GROUND FAULT INTERRUPT (GFI)
A device that measures the current flowing to and from an electrical source. When a difference in current flow is detected (which indicates a leakage of electrical current that could cause an injury), the GFI will kick out, shutting off the flow of electricity.

H

HAZARD COMMUNICATION STANDARD (HCS)
The Hazard Communication Standard is an OSHA regulation that requires employers to inform workers of any chemical hazards on the job and to train workers how to protect themselves from the hazards.

HERBICIDE
Chemical that kills plants.

HYDRAULIC SYSTEM
A system found on tractors and other machines that uses high-pressure oil to raise and lower attachments or implements. This system also powers hydraulic motors that turn reel mowers on certain mowing machines.

I

INDIRECT COSTS
These are the hidden costs of a workplace injury or mishap. For example, time spent filling out insurance forms, efforts to hire a replacement worker, overtime to make up for the lost employee. These costs are generally four to ten times higher than the direct costs of an injury. See direct costs.

INSECTICIDE
Chemical that kills insects.

K

KICKOUT
The reaction of a brush-cutting saw blade hitting a strong tree of other solid object. Brushing-cutting blades can be installed on some heavy-duty line trimmers. If the blade strikes a strong, solid object, the rotation of the blade may push the trimmer and blade back violently.

M

MATERIAL SAFETY DATA SHEETS (MSDS)
A document that has health, safety, cleanup, and other useful information about a chemical product. By law, all chemical manufacturers and distributors must make available an MSDS for every product they sell. Employers are required to have an MSDS on file for all chemicals used in their businesses and to make these MSDSs available to employees.

O

OPERATOR'S MANUAL
An operator's manual not only tells how to operate and maintain equipment, but also gives important safety information. All machine operators should thoroughly read the operator's manual before running a machine. Replacement manuals are usually available from the manufacturer.

OSHA
Occupational Safety and Health Administration. Agency of the U.S. government created to help assure safe and healthy working environments. The agency's rules and regulations apply to any company or individual with one or more employees.

OUTDOOR POWER EQUIPMENT
Handheld, walk-behind, and self-propelled machines that use motors or engines to perform tasks around yards, golf courses, nurseries, and other outdoor work sites.

P

PESTICIDE
Chemical used to kill pests such as insects, rodents, and weeds.

PPE
Personal protective equipment (PPE) is clothing and devices designed to protect workers from injury or illness.

PSI
A measure of pressure. It stands for "pounds per square inch."

PTO
PTO stands for Power Take Off. It is a shaft on a tractor that provides power to an implement or attachment. While tractor PTOs are usually found at the rear of the tractor, some models also have mid- or front-PTOs.

R

ROPS
ROPS stand for Rollover Protective Structure. It is a frame or reinforced cab designed to protect the operator in case of a tractor upset.

S

SAFETY WARNING SIGNS
These are decals found on most machines. They warn of a potential safety hazard and give advice on how to operate the machine safely.

SECOND PARTIES
Individuals other than the machine operator who are in the same area as a machine.

SELECTIVE CONTROL VALVE (SCV)
This is a valve (or valves) on a tractor that controls the hydraulics to an attachment, such as a front-end loader. A lever on the tractor regulates the flow of hydraulic oil from the SCV, through hydraulic hoses, and to the attachment.

T

THREE-POINT HITCH
A standard system, found at the rear of a tractor, for mounting attachments. The system uses three points to mount the attachment. The two points down low are called the lower links, while the one up behind the operator's seat is called the top link. Tractor hydraulics allow the operator to control the height of the 3-point hitch and its attachments.

TONGUE WEIGHT
The weight of the trailer tongue pressing down on the truck's hitch.

TOXICITY
Measurement of how poisonous a chemical or product is.

W

WORKER'S COMPENSATION
Insurance that covers an employee for injuries that happen while he or she is on the job.

INDEX